SCANNERS

SCANNING INTO THE FUTURE

4

SCANNERS
SCANNING INTO THE FUTURE
4

Bill Robertson

NEXUS SPECIAL INTERESTS

Nexus Special Interests Ltd.
Nexus House
Azalea Drive
Swanley
Kent BR8 8HU

First published 1999
Reprinted 1999

ISBN 1-85486-180-8

Typeset by Kate Williams, Abergavenny
Printed and bound in Great Britain by Whitstable Litho Printers Ltd

Contents

Acknowledgements

I couldn't have collated all the information and photos in this book without the help of others – most of whom are fellow scanner enthusiasts.

As well as the original material from Peter Rouse, I must also acknowledge and thank Ian Doyle for his excellent aircraft photos together with Mike Ridley for further help and assistance, Elaine Richards and the many readers of *Radio Active* magazine for their helpful comments and suggestions for this book, and Chris Lorek for his technical measurements and photos of currently available equipment. Thanks also to Richard Rouse (Peter's nephew), Richard Hillier, Stephen Barnes, and the many other correspondents who have also offered advice and input but who wish to 'stay in the background'. If I have forgotten anyone, it's not intentional!

Bill Robertson
March 1999

Peter Rouse (left) chats with fellow enthusiasts at the publisher's stand at the Leicester Radio Rally. The world has lost a great 'helper'.

Foreword – a dedication to Peter Rouse

by Eur Ing Chris Lorek BSc(Hons) C.Eng MIEE G4HCL

It was five years ago when I was invited to write a forward to *Scanners 3*, yet to me it seems just a few months ago. As some readers may know, the author and pioneer of the 'Scanners' series of books, Peter Rouse, is unfortunately no longer with us. Sadly, Peter died on the 29th June 1993 after suffering from leukemia for some time. A well-known writer, Peter was remarkably bright and cheerful throughout his illness and I saw him give real inspiration and hope to fellow sufferers – the happiness he imparted to others around him was tremendous. I was fortunate in living near to where Peter received his hospital treatment, and I was glad that we managed to continue our friendship with frequent meetings.

He underwent two years of 'in and out of hospital' treatment for recurrent bouts of his illness, yet kept his hobby interest alive even from his hospital bed with his radio gear and portable computer. I felt very honoured when I heard that Peter had asked the publishers if I would complete and edit his *Scanners 3* book. But the pioneering work of such a writer will never die, and what you see before you is the continuation of Peter's efforts. In line with the wishes of Peter's family, I'm happy to help to continue the tradition, and have managed to twist the arm of Bill Robertson, who is the UK's foremost writer on the subject of scanners with a continual monthly column on the subject in nationally published radio magazines in the UK for several years, to collate and prepare the material for *Scanners 4*. Much of Peter's work from *Scanners 3* is contained in this book, with updates and additional material where appropriate. Thus, Peter's name and his work will certainly be kept alive, a fitting tribute to someone who helped many get started in the hobby of HF/VHF/UHF listening. The world has lost a great 'helper', and I know that he would wish this book to be dedicated not just to him but also to his wife Val and children James, Abbi, and Arron.

1 ■ Introduction

When Peter Rouse first pounded out the words for the original edition of this book, he never thought he would see so many revisions and reprints in his lifetime. Sadly, Peter left this world a short while before *Scanners 3*, the predecessor to this book, was published, but I'm sure he would have been proud of it. That was because the book had seen the biggest number of changes and additions to the point of a virtual rewrite, with the inclusion of a lot more frequency listings plus more information on coastal stations, airfields and the emergency services, together with the introduction of a section on the HF (Short Wave) bands. This book carries on that tradition, with the addition of several new sections as well as a complete revision and update as necessary of every single earlier chapter. You won't find that much has changed in areas such as radio basics and aerial principles which likewise don't change very much. But some of the subsequent chapters are virtually a complete rewrite, with the addition of a significant amount of new material. But let's start off first with a cautionary note.

WHAT CAN I LEGALLY LISTEN TO?

Typical scanners available on the market today usually cover a very wide frequency range, and as such they're capable of tuning into a similarly wide number of radio transmissions. Like those used by the coastguard and other emergency services, civil and military airband, security guards down at your local hypermarket or shopping centre, taxis, CB operators, radio hams, cellular telephones, pagers, local businesses, the cordless phone used next door, taxis, private investigators, your local pizza delivery service – the list is almost endless.

With the equally wide availability of scanners, many people do indeed

1

have great fun in listening to these as a hobby in itself. Most users are sensible and keep what they hear and do to themselves, whilst others like to make a 'big thing' about what they listen to. The latter sometimes then find their knuckles get rapped! The serious side to this, of course, is that of criminals using what they hear to advantage. Fortunately more and more 'professional' users, such as police forces, are acting on the sensible assumption that if they want their conversations to be private, they must scramble them. Others are still 'open'. I'm often asked "Surely if I don't reveal or act on what I've heard, it's OK, can't I then listen to what I want?".

I make no apologies for reiterating here the caution given in the earlier book; the aim of this book is to provide a basic understanding of the use of scanning receivers and VHF/UHF communications. Contrary to popular belief, this type of equipment is not solely purchased by people who have no legitimate right to listen in to certain kinds of radio traffic and who wish to illegally snoop on other people's messages. Many people from licensed amateurs to commercial and professional users buy this type of equipment for perfectly legitimate reasons. However, such people may still not fully understand how to use the scanner to its best ability. This book is aimed at all scanner users who want a better understanding of how their equipment works. In order to achieve that aim it has been necessary to include a wide range of information, some of which might be considered sensitive. Although certain bands and frequency allocations are shown, the book should not be interpreted as an invitation to listen-in unless the appropriate licence or authority is held.

The UK's Radiocommunications Agency states, at the time of writing (1999), that a licence is not required for a radio receiver as long as it is not capable of transmission as well. The exception to this is that it is an offence to listen to unlicensed broadcasters (pirates) without a licence, and licences are not issued for this purpose. Although it is not illegal to sell, buy or own a scanning or other receiver in the UK, it must only be used to listen to transmissions meant for *general reception*. The services that you can listen to include Amateur and Citizens' Band transmissions, licenced broadcast radio and at sea you may listen to weather and navigation information.

It is an offence to listen to any other radio services unless you are authorised by the Secretary of State to do so.

The responsibility thus lies with you, the equipment owner, to satisfy yourself that you have a legal right to listen-in to any radio transmission. You can get a free information sheet, entitled *Receive Only Radio – Scanners etc.* publication Ref. RA169 which gives comprehensive details, from the Radiocommunications Agency at South Quay Three, 189 Marsh Wall, London E14 9SX Tel: 0171 211 2110 or on the Internet at http://www.open.gov.uk/radiocom/rahome.htm.

All information contained here has been published before at some time, much of it by the government. However, its publication here must not be interpreted as some kind of right to listen-in to anything you wish. However, I was interested to see recently a document from the Department of Trade and Industry (who regulate communication licensing) to police forces which provided advice on seizing scanners. The document said that tuning into airband and marine transmissions could not be considered 'a serious offence'. Even so, I know of one individual who was formally interviewed by the police after simply admitting he used his scanner down at the local airport when plane-spotting with his son.

The UK government has recently been taking a hard line against users of scanners for illegal purposes, and has been known to distribute leaflets giving police officers guidance on what to do if someone is suspected of operating a scanner illegally. A number of such users have been successfully convicted of listening into police transmissions – in one reported case the user was imprisoned. At the other end of the scale, newspapers have got away with printing details of how they deliberately sent their reporters out to monitor cellular conversations, publishing what they heard. If you are in any doubt as to what you are, and are not, allowed to listen to, you should seek guidance from your national radio regulatory body which in the UK is the Radiocommunications Agency (RA). Their free leaflet, *Receive Only Radio – Scanners etc.* (see above) explains the situation in the UK and is available upon request.

WHAT'S CHANGED?

So what has happened since *Scanners 3*? The answer is quite a lot! The use of the radio spectrum, particularly on the VHF and UHF allocations, has changed a great deal over the past years, and plans for further changes are also in hand. As then, the biggest changes have occurred to the VHF and UHF frequency listings. This continues as new services emerge, such as TETRA (Terrestrial Trunked Radio) and Low-Earth-Orbiting (LEO) satellite-based communications systems which can be picked up on a handheld receiver. Details of these are given in new chapters in the book, together with the new frequencies being included in the frequency allocations section of this book. If you should come across a strange-sounding signal on a given channel, a glance at the allocations section will show what that part of the spectrum is allocated to. However, in a similar manner to *Scanners 3* I have not padded out the book with details of what taxi firm operates on what frequency in any given area, or listings of TV and broadcast radio channels and the like.

The frequency spectrum covered by scanners has increased both upwards and downwards, and even handheld scanners now commonly cover down to below 500 kHz, and up to 1300 MHz or even 2000 MHz and above. Scanners have also come down in size, some having the area of a credit card or less if not the thinness of one. Time will no doubt bring further advances in miniaturisation, and there's already a credit card calculator-sized transceiver available with built-in VHF and UHF coverage including AM Airband. Scanners have also increased in sophistication, some having alphanumeric memory channel tagging facilities, bandscopes, and an ever-increasing number of memory channels and search ranges.

Although some years ago, the use of PCs in conjunction with a scanner for control and frequency management was big in the US but not over here, things have changed dramatically. PCs now are very affordable, and many homes contain at least one PC if not more. Not only can these be used with appropriate software to remotely control a scanner, new radios have evolved such as the IC-PCR100, IC-PCR100 and Optocom that are simply 'black boxes', controlled exclusively by a PC with a 'virtual front panel' being displayed on the PC screen.

Computer-based communication has also increased, and trunked radio systems are now commonplace. This is where conversations seem to hop about between channels, often confusing the scanner user, although there are now 'intelligent' scanners available which can automatically track some of these systems.

The huge increase in the use of personal pagers has come about by the popularity of 'calling party pays' pager systems. Here, the pager user pays a relatively low one-off price for the pager itself, with no monthly or annual service fee. Instead, the caller to the pager pays a premium for the call. Both numerical and alphanumeric systems are in use, and readily available freeware and shareware PC software programs are available to decode these with the PC linked to your receiver via either a simple interface or through a PC sound card. Likewise, software for decoding other signalling, such as CTCSS (sub-audible tones) and DTMF (Dual Tone Medium Frequency, i.e. 'Touch Tone') is readily available. Similarly, for off-air weather fax transmissions from low-earth orbiting and geostationary satellites.

As predicted in the last book, the use of encryption, i.e. speech scrambling, is increasing as radio users have finally had it knocked into their heads that if they blindly transmit, it would rather naïve to think that their conversations are totally private. Some users, such as the police, naturally have a need for privacy of communication in order to prevent criminals overhearing their conversations, although at the time of writing a number of forces have scrapped scrambling due to poor on-air results and are using other means such GSM cellphones when needed for confidential communication. Scanner manufacturers haven't been slow to respond, and there are at least two handheld scanners plus one base scanner with the ability to decode the simpler inverted speech methods of scrambling.

The communications scene will inevitably continue to change with new innovations, and I hope this book will help you to get the best out of your receiver, whether you use it for hobby or professional monitoring purposes.

2 **Understanding radio**

No mathematics, no theory, no problems. If you are new to the hobby then have a browse through this chapter, because it answers the queries most frequently raised by scanner owners who are not familiar with VHF and UHF communications. First of all let us look at what we mean by VHF and UHF. The entire radio spectrum stretches from long wave upwards and as we go higher in frequency so different parts of the spectrum are given different names. The best way to imagine it is to think of a very long tuning scale on a radio. At the left side we have long wave, then comes medium. From then on we talk in terms of frequency rather than waves. Note that there is a fixed relationship between wavelength and frequency and it is always possible to determine the wavelength of any given frequency or vice versa. So a look at Table 2.1 will show how things progress beyond medium wave. Next comes Medium Frequency (MF), then High Frequency (HF) which is also still known as short wave. From 30 MHz (megahertz) to 300 MHz we have Very High Frequency (VHF) and between 300 MHz and 3000 MHz we have Ultra High Frequency (UHF). It is these latter two parts of the spectrum that we are mainly interested in as these are the bands covered by most scanners. Look again at Table 2.1 and you will see reference to both kHz (kilohertz) and MHz and it is useful to understand the relationship between the two. They are simply measurements and the kilo and mega parts are the same as those applied to measuring metric length and weight. Kilo means a thousand times and mega means a million times, so 1000 kHz is exactly the same as 1 MHz. Understanding this will help you grasp the idea of what is known as tuning or stepping rates on your scanner. Scanners are not tuned like an ordinary radio. If you want to alter a frequency up or down you will have to do it in small jumps. Often the scanner will tune in 5 or 10 kHz increments but those designed specifically for the British market will often have 12.5 kHz increments because this is a common British channel spacing.

Table 2.1 Radio frequency spectrum, each division as a frequency range

Frequency division	Frequency range
Very low frequency (VLF)	3–30 kHz
Low frequency (LF)	30–300 kHz
Medium frequency (MF)	300–3000 kHz
High frequency (HF)	3–30 MHz
Very high frequency (VHF)	3–300 MHz
Ultra high frequency (UHF)	300–3000 MHz
Super high frequency (SHF)	3–30 GHz
Extremely high frequency (EHF)	30–300 GHz
No designation	300–3000 GHz

k =kilo = ×1,000; M = mega = ×1,000,000; G = giga = ×1,000,000,000

CHANNELS

Channelising is something which often confuses newcomers and yet it is quite simple. We can take any part of the radio spectrum and divide it up into small blocks. A look at Figure 2.1 will show how this is done. In most countries, the authorities determine how the channel spacing will work. It is common in Britain on the bands used for emergency services and Private Mobile Radio (PMR) to use channelising, rather than allocate frequencies to users at random. Typical spacing in Britain is 12.5 kHz but in the USA and other countries the spacing is usually 10 kHz. This can present problems for some scanner owners who have receivers designed for the American market, because they cannot tune exactly onto the right frequency of many British channels. For example it is not possible to enter the frequency 144.7625 on some scanners although dialling in 144.760 may be close enough to hear the signal: it varies from one model to another. It is a point to watch when buying a scanner.

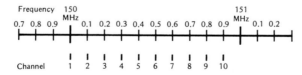

Figure 2.1 Channelising. Any section of the radio spectrum can be divided up and each spot frequency given a channel number.

DISTANCE

How far will a signal travel? Why can I hear an airport control tower 30 miles away but not my own airport which is just over the hill behind my house? These are typical of the questions from newcomers. VHF and UHF signals travel nowhere near as far as medium and long wave signals – in fact they only travel over what is known as 'line of sight', typically 20 to 30 miles. In practice the distance can be far less or much greater depending on circumstances. One factor is the power output of the station we are listening to. A base station with between 25 and 50 watts output power may come in loud and clear over a given distance but a small walkie-talkie with only a fraction of a watt output might not cover the same distance.

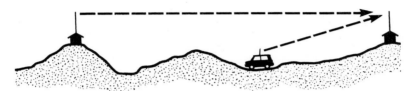

Figure 2.2 Ground wave. Typically line of sight at VHF and UHF.

You should also bear in mind that VHF and UHF signals are easily blocked by obstructions such as high buildings, hills and even trees. There are also strange weather -based conditions that can cause signals to travel massive distances – one of these is known as Sporadic-E. VHF signals do not normally bounce back to Earth off the ionosphere (the effect that causes HF signals to travel great distances) but on occasion the E-layer of the ionosphere thickens up and the signals do bounce back. Another effect is known as tropospheric ducting. This happens when

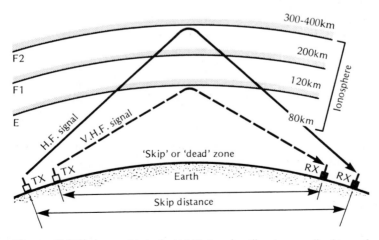

Figure 2.3 Sky wave. Note that VHF signals will not normally skip as far as HF signals.

cold and warm air streams meet at about 2 kilometres above the Earth's surface. A conductive layer is formed that can act as a sort of pipe for signals and send them considerable distances (several thousand kilometres in some cases). This effect is often associated with high barometric pressure and fog and the effect is often seen in the summer when it can cause television interference.

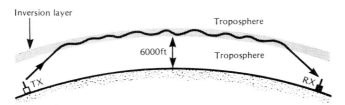

Figure 2.4 Tropospherical ducting 'Tropo'.

MODES

There are several ways of imposing speech (and music and television pictures) onto a radio signal. For speech the three common methods are Frequency Modulation (FM), Amplitude Modulation (AM) and Single Sideband (SSB). You don't need to understand the technical difference between the modes but you must appreciate that they are different and your scanner must have different circuits to cope with the different modes. For instance all transmissions in the international VHF aircraft band use AM, and if your scanner is tuned to a station but FM mode is selected, you will hear nothing or at best a very distorted signal. Britain is one of the few places in the world now that uses AM mode for communications outside the aircraft band, for example, in a given area you are likely to find both AM and FM transmissions being used in a PMR band. Most countries (particularly the USA) exclusively use FM with its many advantages. If you want to pick up a wide selection of transmissions then you need a scanner that allows you to select FM or AM regardless of the frequency you are tuned to. Many scanners now allow you to store a frequency into memory along with the mode. However, you will find several scanners on the UK market which do not allow you to do this. Notably scanners designed for the American market have no FM/AM select button and instead automatically switch to FM on any frequency except the airband when they switch to AM.

Single sideband is a rather specialised mode and is divided into upper and lower sidebands. To resolve SSB your scanner needs special circuitry and this is only found on a handful of models. The mode is used by amateurs on the VHF and UHF bands, as well as a wide range of utility stations on HF. Models of scanners with HF coverage as well as SSB reception facilities can thus bring in an extra area of interesting listening.

SIMPLEX AND DUPLEX

A question that's often raised by newcomers to VHF/UHF communications is why can they only hear one of two stations who are communicating with each other. This is because they may be using either split frequency simplex or duplex. First though, let's start at the beginning and look at the simplest arrangement which is called simplex.

A typical example of single frequency simplex is the international aircraft band between 118 and 137 MHz. A control tower for example may be operating on 119.950 MHz and the aircraft will also transmit on exactly the same frequency. Assuming that both are within reception range of your scanner then you will hear both sides of the conversation on the single frequency of 119.95 MHz. However, some transmissions use a pair of frequencies with the base transmitting on one frequency but with mobile stations on another – this is split frequency simplex. In this instance the transmitters and receivers will have to be tuned to the appropriate frequencies. The scanner user will need to enter both frequencies into the scanner and switch between them to hear both sides of the conversation. Some upmarket scanners have this 'duplex frequency listen' ability by the press of a button.

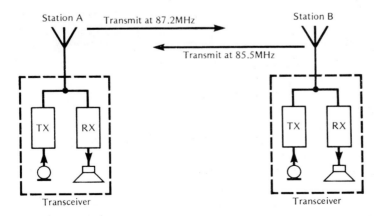

Figure 2.5 Split frequency simplex.

REPEATERS

Some users who need to obtain greater range for their communications rely on what are known as repeaters. These transmitters/receivers are normally situated on high ground and have the added advantage of allowing one mobile unit to talk to another. Where the police use such systems this is known as 'Talkthrough'. Repeaters work on split frequencies, in other words the 'input' or receiver frequency is usually several megahertz away from the transmit or 'output frequency'. The transmitter normally is switched off but when the repeater's receiver picks up a signal it then activates the transmitter and the audio output of the receiver is fed to the input of the transmitter and so rebroadcasts it. In practice the receiver will not respond to just any signal but also requires a valid tone. On amateur repeaters this is a simple audible tone burst of 1750 Hz that is detected by a circuit in the repeater. On commercial systems as well as some UK amateur repeaters sub-audible tones are used (known as CTCSS) and the commercial repeaters may be programmed to respond to several different tones. This is the case where more than one operator is using the repeater. The system is often referred to as a community repeater and can be used by several companies or organisations. Each has its own CTCSS tone and the access circuits are not only fitted to the

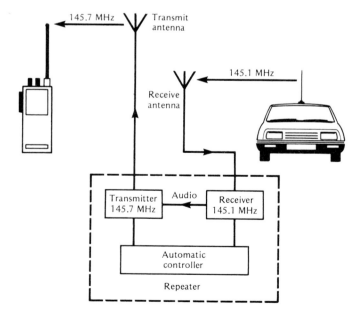

Figure 2.6 Repeater. Automatic turn-on and turn-off. In the case of talkthrough the switching controller is operated manually.

repeater but also the individual mobile or handheld transceivers. In that way the various users only hear calls from their own base station or mobiles.

In order to monitor calls on a repeater system you only need to tune to the repeater output frequency. A variation on this theme is what are known as trunked systems. This is where a network of repeaters is used and controlled by computer. A typical network may cover most of the country and so a base station can call its mobiles as long as they are within range of any of the trunked repeaters.

You can read a more in-depth description of the above, plus details on trunking, selective calling, etc. in Chapter 5 *Radio systems explained*.

3 The hardware

So what is a scanner? The simple answer is that it is a radio receiver which is capable of tuning into radio frequency channels that you won't normally find on your ordinary domestic radio. What also sets it apart from a manually tuned radio is that it will also look automatically through dozens or even hundreds or thousands of channels looking for radio signals. Unlike broadcast transmissions those frequencies will only carry occasional conversations and so the scanner constantly sweeps through its memory channels and only stops when it finds an active one. Once the transmission ends the scanner then resumes sweeping its pre-programmed channels looking for another active one.

These days all scanners are what's known as synthesised types. The very earliest scanners used quartz crystals to control reception of each one of the frequencies that the owner wished to receive. A typical early scanner may have had around 12 available channels and appropriate crystals had to be plugged into sockets inside the equipment. In order to change a frequency it was necessary to order a replacement crystal which had been specially cut or tuned. Many old crystal-controlled types are occasionally seen on the secondhand market, but these days it is the synthesised type of scanner that dominates the market as these allow much greater flexibility. Not only can the required frequency be entered on a keypad but the ability to store the frequency in a computer-style memory has meant that many more channels can be stored even in a small handheld scanner. The simplest scanners may only have the capacity to store between about 10 and 50 channels which sometimes need to be manually pre-programmed by you to the frequencies that you want to monitor.

The more sophisticated scanners now also allow such things as mode and a short alphanumeric name to be stored along with the frequency, so that once the scanner is put to work it automatically switches to the correct mode for the frequency concerned and reminds you of what you have programmed the channel to receive. All of this is made possible by a simple and compact microprocessor within the scanner and in most instances it allows for even greater sophistication. For example it is usually possible to set the scanner searching between a low and upper frequency limit so allowing you to discover new channels that may be in operation in your area.

YOU GET WHAT YOU PAY FOR

Newcomers to the scanning hobby often ask what the difference is between a cheap scanner and another costing a small fortune – the answer is facilities. Some of the Tandy/Realistic handheld scanners are probably the cheapest and simplest scanners on the market. The lowest cost type has just 10 memory channels, limited frequency coverage, no search facility and is FM only. I must stress that, despite that, it may well fill the needs of someone who, for example, only wants to monitor a handful of marine channels. At the other end of the scale are the Icom IC-R-7100, IC-R9000 and AOR 3000A with very wide band coverage and good front-end filtering. This latter facility is often not understood by scanner owners and it's worthwhile looking briefly at what it involves.

In any given area there will be a vast number of radio signals travelling through the airwaves – everything from powerful broadcast transmissions to weak communications signals. The less expensive scanners will simply amplify all these signals in what are known as the radio frequency, or RF, stages of its circuitry before passing the signals to those parts of the circuit that at any given moment select the required signal which eventually passes through to the loudspeaker. In practice, the RF amplification is usually divided into at least two separate stages, one for the lower frequency coverage and one for the upper. However, what can happen is that strong signals that you do not wish to hear can interfere with the scanner circuitry and block out those signals you are trying to listen to. In severe cases, several undesirable effects may be introduced into the scanner's circuit. Typical examples are blocking, reciprocal mixing and inter-modulation distortion. One of the most obvious effects is where you are listening to a transmission and it suddenly seems to stop for no apparent reason. What has probably happened is that a very strong signal has appeared on a slightly different frequency and has desensitised the scanner causing the squelch to close.

Another undesirable effect that can occur is when two or more strong signals appear to upset the scanner's mixing circuits. This can often be identified by a signal suddenly breaking through on a frequency which you know is incorrect for that transmission. For example, at some locations in built-up areas with plenty of PMR and cellular transmitters, a certain mixture of transmissions together with, say, a local radio FM broadcast can cause the latter station to appear on some channels of your scanner. Of course the signal is not really there, the internal mixing circuits in the scanner are being overloaded and cause this effect. The way that the above problems can be overcome is to have more selective circuits in the scanner's RF stage. Tuned filters ensure that only the desired signals are passed to the tuning and mixing stages. As the scanner steps through each frequency in its memory, so the correct filter is selected or the RF stages are electronically tuned to peak at that frequency. Naturally all of this makes the scanner more complex and so more expensive. The added components also make the set bulkier and that is why most small handheld scanners do not incorporate much in the way of front-end filtering. Owners of handhelds now know why their equipment often suffers problems when connected to an outside aerial such as a discone or a wideband amplified vertical type. The RF stages are presented with stronger signals than they are designed to cope with.

SWITCHES, KNOBS, SOCKETS AND THINGS THAT GO CLICK AND SQUEAK

The average scanner presents a bewildering array of facilities for anyone not used to communications equipment. However, most of the facilities are fairly straightforward although some handbooks do leave a lot to be desired in the way they explain them. Let us have a look at some of the things you will find on most scanners – I have not included the obvious ones such as volume.

Squelch or mute

This is an electronic switch that cuts noise to the loudspeaker when no signal is being received. It also serves the important function on a scanner of telling the set that transmissions have stopped, so please start scanning again. You need to set the squelch by turning it to the point where, with no signal being received, the loudspeaker cuts out. It is important to note that you should never advance the squelch any further than is necessary. The more you turn it, the more you desensitise the scanner to the point where it will only respond to very strong signals – the weak ones will be missed. In practice, don't be surprised if the squelch needs adjusting for different bands. For instance, you may find that having set the squelch correctly for a signal at 80 megahertz, the squelch suddenly opens when it hops to a frequency at 170 megahertz. This is quite normal – in any given area there may well be bands where there is a small amount of background noise that will need the squelch to be advanced a bit further to get it to close. Some scanners offer a variety of types of squelch including one where even if lack of background noise opens the squelch, the scanner will continue to hunt through its memories unless there is sound such as a voice present (often known as voice-scan). My personal experience is that this facility rarely works very well. One further facility is scan delay. Sometimes you do not want the scanner to resume scanning until you have heard any replies to a transmission. Scan delay allows for a small lag before scanning commences so that you can catch the reply. Only when the scan delay period is exceeded with no further transmissions does the circuitry recommence scanning.

Search

With this facility, no-one's frequency is safe from you. Let us assume that you have a sneaking suspicion that interesting transmissions are taking place in your area between 160 and 170 megahertz. Now because of the intermittent nature of communications transmissions it can be like looking for a needle in a haystack to discover which actual frequencies are in use so get the scanner to do the hard work. On many machines it is possible to select a lower and upper search limit and leave the scanner to sweep between those two frequencies. Naturally, it will stop when it finds something. A further refinement on this appears on higher-class scanners when the scanner can automatically also store the frequencies it finds into a spare memory bank for you. This means you can even go off for the day and come back and see which frequencies were active.

Stepping rates

Searching is always done in conjunction with stepping rates. Unlike a conventional radio, a scanner does not have infinite degrees of tuning. In other words as it goes up or down in frequency, it does it in small 'hops'. The steps available on the scanner are important because they may prevent you from properly tuning into the correct frequency. In the UK we use 12.5 kHz channel spacing and that can be a problem for scanners that can only tune in 5 or 10 kHz steps. What will usually happen is that when you try to enter the correct digits and press the Enter key, the scanner's circuit will round the number up or down to suit its available stepping rate. In the worst case this means that you are slightly off-tuned from the frequency you want, and will either not hear the required signal or it will be distorted. At best, the scanner's filters may be fairly broad band and you will still receive the signals with little difficulty. Again, the above should be noted when choosing a scanner and you should be aware that the previously mentioned units designed for the American market may well not have 12.5 kHz stepping rates. At the time of writing, VHF airband is due to progress towards 8.33 kHz spacing, and only two scanners are currently capable of this step rate. However the transition will take several years, but I would advise checking the current situation with your dealer prior to purchase if VHF airband is part of your listening interests, to ensure the scanner is capable of being programmed to this spacing for tuning and searching.

Priority channel

Some scanners include what is known as a priority channel and indeed may have more than one. This channel or channels are scanned more frequently than the others and the idea is that the most important frequencies are assigned to the priority positions.

Bandwidth and mode

Many scanners can receive a number of modes, the most common being FM or NFM, WFM, and AM. NFM is usually used to indicate Narrowband FM with WFM as Wideband FM, to differentiate between the two. The difference is in the receiver bandwidth filtering, NFM is used for two-way communications whereas WFM is used for high-quality broadcast sound, i.e. on the 88–108 MHz Band II broadcast band and for UHF TV sound. Weather satellites are a halfway house though, and use a wider FM deviation greater than that used for two-way communication, but narrower than that for WFM. Receivers with NFM (or just FM is it's often called in receivers dedicated to communications use) need to reject signals 25 kHz, and preferably 12.5 kHz, away from the tuned frequency. Scanners such as those from AOR, Icom and Yupiteru do normally have such tight filtering and offer good results on the communications bands, but these are often too narrow for good results on weather satellites. In my experience, those from Realistic/Tandy/Netset etc. usually have wider filtering to primarily accommodate FM use in the US rather than the narrower FM deviation used in Europe. Although they might not give as good rejection of 12.5 kHz spaced signals, the results on weather satellite reception in NFM mode are somewhat better.

When choosing a scanner, do remember the comments in Chapter 2. Some scanners sold in the UK do not allow you to select the mode at all. Equipment designed primarily for the American market always assumes that transmissions outside the aircraft band will be FM mode. In the UK however, both AM and FM are used.

On some more upmarket scanners a further facility is single sideband (SSB) and depending on the scanner very narrow-band circuits may be employed for this mode. SSB uses a system where the carrier of a double-sideband AM signal together with one of the sidebands is removed before being transmitted, and the missing carrier is reinserted in the receiver. As each of the sidebands, one being the lower sideband (LSB) and the other being the upper sideband (USB) are in fact a mirror image of each other, you will get fully readable reception from either.

Tuning in an SSB signal requires a degree of practice though. It will initially sound like a Donald Duck-type audio, and very careful tuning, in fine 100 Hz or 50 Hz tuning steps, is needed. After approximately tuning to the signal, switch to the fine tuning steps if you haven't already done so and carefully tune up and down until the tone of the received speech sounds as natural as possible. If you can't get any intelligence at all, even though it seems to be speech you're receiving, then switch from LSB to USB or USB to LSB and try again. Commercial users inevitably use USB for speech, while amateurs use LSB on radio frequencies below 10 MHz and USB on those above 10 MHz.

RF attenuator

This is a switch (it may be marked Local/DX) that allows you to desensitise the scanner. Remember the earlier comments about strong signals upsetting the tuning stages – this facility will reduce or can even eliminate the problem. Unfortunately the side-effect is that it will also cut down the weaker signals so that you can probably no longer hear them. Even so, in extreme cases it can be useful and at least allow you to hear some transmissions, whereas the scanner may otherwise permanently lock-up because of overload.

Tape control

This is coupled to the squelch circuit and will automatically switch a tape recorder on when transmissions are received. It is only available on the more expensive base models.

Memory backup

One point to note with many, but not all, scanners is that the memory that stores all the frequencies often utilises what is sometimes known as volatile RAM (random access memory), or VRAM. In order for the information to be retained while the scanner is switched off it is necessary to keep a small amount of power running to the memory chips. This is done either by having a separate battery or batteries to provide memory power or the inclusion of a small lithium cell in the circuit. These cells will not last forever and from time to time will need to be replaced. It is always a good idea to keep a list of all the frequencies and modes you have stored in each memory, providing of course you are allowed to listen to these, because the day may well come when you switch on and find that everything has gone blank. It is worth noting that sometimes the loss of backup power can also cause the scanner to behave in an odd way. If it has lost all memory and fails to operate correctly even when all data has been re-entered then it may still mean that the system needs to be reset by the inclusion of a new backup cell. Newer scanners sometimes employ a better solution, that of EAROM (Electrically Alterable Read Only Memory), which stores all your changes electrically into a memory IC which doesn't need a backup for information retention. But note here that sometimes the EAROM is electrically written only the instant you manually switch the scanner off each time. So, if you let your scanner's battery pack go flat, or disconnect it, while the scanner is still switched on then you may lose the information you have changed, i.e. new frequencies stored or altered during that operating session.

Computer control

AOR, Yaesu and Icom currently all offer scanners with the necessary sockets for computer control, although in some cases you'll need an optional interface to connect the scanner to the RS-232 port of your PC. As well as commercial software, there is an increasing amount of shareware software available on a 'try before you buy' basis. Another use for the computer control port is to couple a frequency searcher such as the Optoelectronics Scout to the scanner – when the searcher finds a nearby frequency it can automatically tune your receiver to that frequency.

NO SCANNER BUT STILL WANT TO LISTEN?

You don't necessarily need to own a scanner receiver if you want to have a listen around on the airwaves. At the time of writing, the Internet is evolving in an explosive way, and one use of this has been for audio-based relay. There are already a number of web sites in existence, and by the time this book is read I'm sure there will be many more, which carry live audio from various police and airport radio systems in the US and other countries. A mouse click on the appropriate hyperlink then results in live received audio from the service in question coming from your multimedia PC's speakers. An extension of this are the scanner enthusiasts' sites, with a remotely controlled scanner receiver and aerial system ready installed and controlled by the host computer linked to the Internet. Here you can enter the frequency or frequencies you wish to listen to directly, or select one of a number of frequency from a 'menu' list at the remote end. With the expansion of the Internet, who knows what else will become available in just another year?

4 Aerials

Nearly all scanners are supplied with some sort of aerial to get you going. With the exception of handheld types that is about all the telescopic ones are good for. To get the best out of your base or mobile scanner you will need to invest in a proper aerial (antenna is essentially the same for non-UK language readers). You will also need to connect between aerial and scanner using the proper type of cable. It can never be stressed enough that an outside aerial mounted as high as possible is an essential part of the receiving system. We are dealing with low-level communications signals and so we need to gather every bit of them that we can. A proper aerial system will pull in signals that you will never hear just using a telescopic whip attached to the scanner. If you use an external aerial then note that you must disconnect the telescopic as leaving it in circuit will upset the input impedance to the equipment.

VHF/UHF AERIALS

The aerial needed for a scanner must not be confused with the long wire types used for other types of radio reception. This is a very specialised area and the aerial and cable must be well sited and in good condition. Signals are subject to high losses at these frequencies and even minor defects in the system will almost certainly degrade performance. VHF/UHF aerials fall into two broad categories: broadband and narrowband. The former performs well across a wide range of frequencies and the latter is suited to one particular band. The narrowband type should not be ignored as it has its uses, for instance where the air and marine bands are concerned it may well perform much better than a broadband type. The broadband aerial is in fact something of a compromise.

It is also advisable that you understand about polarisation. This

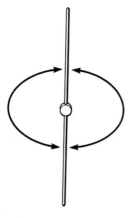

Figure 4.1 Vertical polarisation. Pick-up pattern is in all directions.

simply means that transmission or reception takes place via elements that are either vertical to the ground or horizontal. Most communications take place using vertically polarised aerials and for optimum reception the scanner aerial should also be polarised the same way. The occasional exception to the rule is with some amateur transmissions and commercial communications between two fixed points. The disadvantage of using horizontally polarised transmission for most communications is that horizontal aerials are usually directional to one degree or another. This is hardly desirable where mobile communications are concerned because the signals can come from any direction.

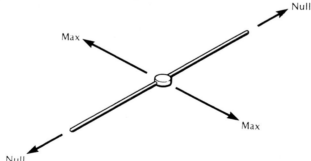

Figure 4.2 Horizontal polarisation. The aerial is sensitive in two directions on and picks up very little end-on.

NARROWBAND AERIALS

The simplest narrowband aerial is the quarter wave element or whip, and it is possible to trim a whip to match the frequency in use. You must note that the input impedance to the scanner will be the standard 50 ohms.

Using a standard formula of 75 divided by the frequency in MHz to give the length of a quarter wave in metres, you can work out what the length of a whip should be, but note that you must reduce it by 5 per cent to produce the 50 ohm match. If you mismatch then some signal will be lost.

Note that the aerial will work at its best and be 50-ohm matched only when it is mounted above a ground plane such as a vehicle body or rod radials. Although this is technically a narrowband aerial it will provide good receive performance over several MHz and is ideal for marine or air bands. This type of aerial can easily be made from the parts of old TV or broadcast FM radio antennas. A further simple aerial is the dipole (Fig 4.4) with each 'leg' being a quarter wave whip.

A refinement is the ⅝ whip which can provide a few decibels of gain and so give even better performance – you may have seen this type of aerial mounted on emergency vehicles where a long whip terminates in a small black coil close to the mounting unit.

Typical ground plane aerial. This one is designed for airband and the 'drooping' radials give a better 50 ohm match.

25

BROADBAND AERIALS

These are by far the most popular aerials for scanner use and can be sub-divided into two types: active and passive. The most popular is an aerial known as a discone, and despite what some advertisements claim by suppliers this is a vertically polarised aerial even though the top elements are mounted horizontally. It is what happens between the top and bottom elements that determines the polarisation.

The discone is a reasonable compromise for broadband use although it must be noted that at any given frequency it will not be as good as a quarter wave despite some of the exaggerated claims made for its performance. A variation on the discone incorporates an additional top element

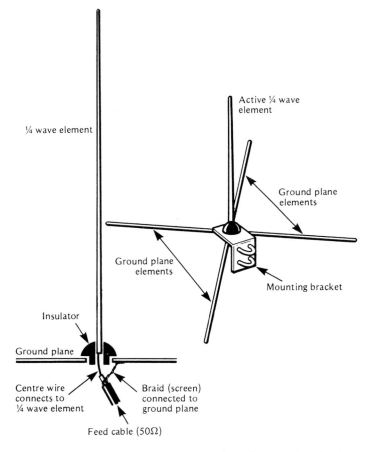

Figure 4.3 Whip aerial. The ground plane can be a steel car body or in the case of a base aerial can be quarter wave long rods.

which is often a ⅝ wave whip for a specific band such as the amateur 2m band.

Another broadband type for scanner use is what is known as the nest of dipoles. Strictly speaking this is a multiband aerial rather than broadband one, as its peak performance occurs when the dimensions of the elements act as half-wave dipoles. This aerial should not be confused with discones that are offered with multiple elements on top. A discone is vertically polarised despite the fact that the top elements are horizontal. Staying with multiband aerials are what are known as the sleeved types. These will not usually perform as well as the two aerials mentioned above but are less obtrusive. A good example of this type is the Scanmaster range from Nevada.

Finally comes the log periodic. This is a multi-element dipole and for correct use must be operated with an aerial rotator, because it is direc-

This discone uses staggered length elements to achieve wider coverage.

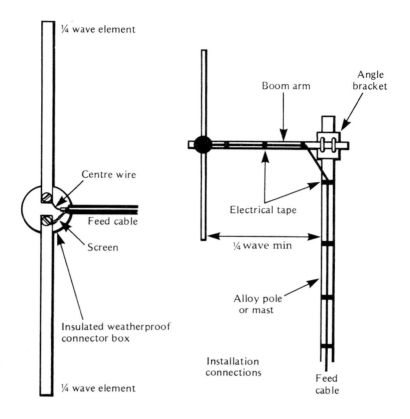

Figure 4.4 The dipole. Vertically polarised, it provides good all-round reception.

tional. Commercial ones usually cover 105–1300 MHz and 50–1300 MHz and offer several dB gain over a discone. The problem of course is that they are directional, but in some cases this can be an advantage if the majority of required signals are being received from approximately the same direction.

MOBILE AERIALS

The true broadband vehicle aerial has yet to be invented, however, compromises are obtained in a number of ways. The first is to use a series of coils along a whip aerial and depending on frequency these can act as resonators or chokes, appearing high impedance or electrically transparent. The result is a complex multiband aerial. There are a number of wideband types available from the radio trade, including a glass-mounted type which doesn't need a hole drilled or clamps/magnetic mount to be used which could otherwise damage the coax cable as it enters your car via the door seal. The second alternative is to use a nominal 100 MHz whip and provide broadband amplification at the base. Finally, an interesting solution comes from Tandy who offer an adapter that allows your car radio aerial to feed your scanner as well. Tandy claim the adapter (which is inexpensive and requires no power) has no effect on the car radio but there must always be some compromise involved. But then, either you are going to listen to the broadcast radio or you're going to listen to the scanner – surely not both – so a simple coaxial aerial switch could be used instead. The final point concerns the scanner aerial plug. It's usually a Motorola type on car radio leads so if you are using a typical scanner you'll need to change it to a BNC type.

HF AERIALS

A common problem found on HF (short wave) by owners of wide-coverage scanners, and even dedicated HF-only receivers, is that when an external long-wire aerial is connected to the set, rather than hearing a lot more they end up with a mush of indecipherable signals. This is often the case with sets such as the small Yupiteru MVT-7200 and AOR AR-8000 handheld scanners, which in all fairness are designed to be compact, self-contained sets primarily designed for use with their set-top aerial. Unfortunately, HF reception is often a little better than useless with this, so the natural inclination is to attach a purpose-designed HF aerial, which is when the problems start! So, what can be done?

Switching in the set's built-in attenuator, if fitted, can often help tremendously, although this also reduces the strength of the wanted signal. For good out-of-band rejection, some form of extra front-end selectivity is usually needed. You can do this by adding an external manually-tuned pre-selector. This fits in-line between your aerial and receiver, and can sometimes also incorporate a matching unit to allow a high impedance long-wire aerial to be connected as well as coax-fed types.

There are a number of HF receive pre-selectors available, from dealers listed at the rear of this book. Adding such a unit will often virtually transform your wideband scanner's performance on HF. If you're in the market for an off-the-shelf unit rather than building one yourself, why not take your receiver along to your local ham radio or scanner dealer and try one of their units on their HF aerial system for yourself before committing yourself? You may be pleasantly surprised, and you'll probably be tempted to come away with a new 'toy'!

AERIALS FOR PORTABLES

A hand-portable scanner can be used with virtually any type of mobile or base aerial and the consequent performance will be better than any small aerial that is normally attached directly to the scanner. However, use of such aerials defeats the portability feature of the scanner. Some portable scanners are supplied with only a small length of wire to act as an aerial. These are probably the poorest aerials as they can rarely be kept in an upright position. A far better choice is the use of a telescopic or helical, and to this end most portable scanners have a BNC type, or more recently a smaller SMA socket, for an external aerial. By far the most common aerial used on portable scanners is the helical whip.

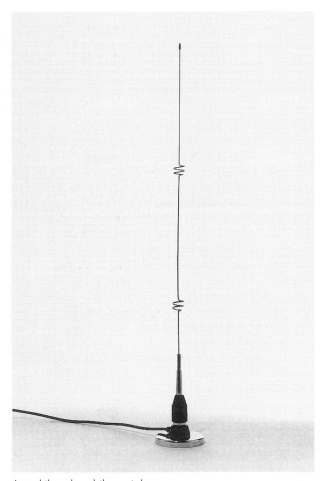

A multiband mobile aerial.

Helicals (rubber ducks)

A helical aerial comprises a metal spring, shrouded in rubber or plastic. They are often seen on walkie-talkies and offer the advantage that unlike a telescopic they are flexible and not easily broken. In practice, the spring usually consists of a metal wire wound over a width of about 10mm. The top part is sometimes stretched out slightly but often the lower end is fairly close wound so as to provide correct impedance matching with the scanner.

Helicals offer better performance than the loose-wire aerial of the same length, are very compact and portable, do not easily break and, being far shorter than respective telescopic aerials, are less likely to do personal damage like poking someone's eye out. However, it is likely that a telescopic aerial will give better performance.

Whatever kind of aerial is used, remember that if the scanner is kept in a pocket or any other position close to the body, the performance will be reduced. Not only does the body act as a screen but the sheer mass can upset the aerial impedance. Portable scanners do not work very well inside vehicles or buildings – in each case it should be possible to attach an external aerial to the set to improve performance. In the case of mobile operation a magnetically mounted aerial can be useful.

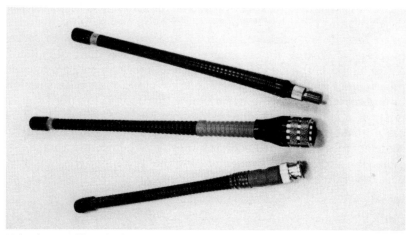

Helicals or 'rubber ducks'. Ideal for handheld scanners, they are available with BNC, PL259 and screw-in connectors.

COAXIAL CABLE

All base and mobile aerials need to be connected to the scanner using screened coaxial cable. However, any old cable that you have lying around might not be suitable. There are several types of coaxial cable available, some for aerials, others for audio and hi-fi use. The latter are unsuitable as are cables designed for use with a normal car radio. The remaining aerial cables fall into two sections, 50 ohm and 75 ohm impedance types. Cable impedance is most critical. The 50 ohm variety is normally used to connect professional, commercial, amateur and CB aerials while 75 ohm cable is used for domestic VHF radio and television – you must use the right one for your scanner. The scanner instruction manual should tell you which cable impedance to use, invariably 50 ohm. This is available from amateur and CB radio dealers, but like the 75 ohm types two main kinds are available: normal or low loss. If the scanner is only being used for VHF reception and only about 8 or 10 metres of cable is to be used then normal cable can be used. However, if UHF reception or long cable lengths are required then low-loss cable is needed, even though this is thicker and less flexible than the lower cost and higher loss type.

Cable construction

Whatever kind of coaxial cable you use, it will have roughly the construction shown in Figure 4.5. Starting at the middle is the core wire, which carries the signal, shrouded in a plastic insulator. The insulator prevents the core from touching the outer braid, which is wound in such a way as to provide an earthed screen for the core. This screen serves two purposes: it ensures that the correct impedance is maintained along the entire length of the cable and it stops any interference from reaching the inner core. Finally, the entire cable is covered in plastic insulation. It is important when installing an aerial that this outer insulation is intact, and not torn or gouged so that the braid is exposed. Rainwater getting into the cable in such circumstances will almost certainly ruin the cable. As the screen of the cable is earthed, it is important when connecting the cable to either the aerial or the connector plug that the inner wire and the braid wire never touch. If they do, the incoming signal is earthed, and so lost.

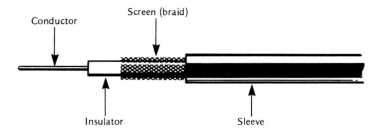

Figure 4.5 Coaxial cable.

Connectors

In order to plug the aerial cable into the scanner you will need appropriate connectors. If you intend to fit your own then note that you usually will need a soldering iron: twisted wires or wires poked into sockets will almost certainly lead to signal losses. Several types of plug are in common use and are shown in Figure 4.6. Some 'solderless' connectors are also

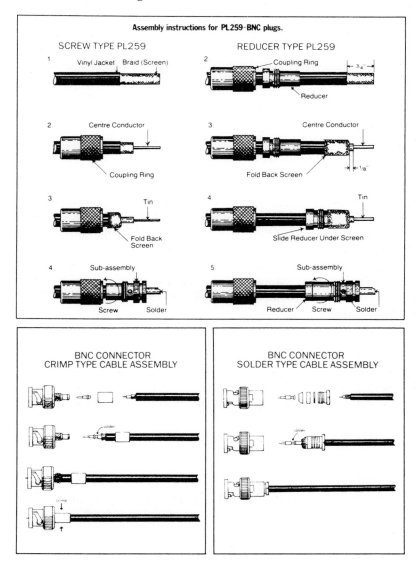

Figure 4.6 Various plugs and connectors (courtesy SSE (UK)).

available, and it is also possible to purchase adapters so that an aerial which has one type of plug can be connected to a scanner which takes another type.

PL259

Commonly found on CB sets and amateur HF and VHF equipment, PL259 connectors are only occasionally encountered on scanners, usually of the older variety. However, they are used extensively to connect to aerials. For instance a socket for a PL259 plug will be found on the base of many discones and amplified verticals.

The plug comes in several varieties, some of which are easier to fit than others. The simplest are designed for use with the thinner, standard (non low-loss), cable. The cable is trimmed, about a quarter inch of braid is left and folded back over the outer insulator. The cable is then pushed into the plug and the braiding and insulator screwed into the plug's shell. Once fully home, the centre conductor is then soldered or crimped depending on the plug type.

Other types of PL259 have a separate inner sleeve which is either a wide or narrow type depending on the coaxial cable used. This type of plug can be fitted to thicker, low-loss cables and the appropriate sleeve is purchased separately. When fitting, the braid must be worked back over the sleeve, the inner conductor is then soldered in the normal way. It is a good idea with both types of plug to expose more centre conductor than is needed. The surplus can be snipped off after fitting.

PL259 plugs have an outer shell that is internally threaded and when mated with the socket, this shell is screwed up tight to ensure firm contact.

BNC

This is the type most commonly found on scanners. It is much smaller than the PL259 and is the connector often found on professional communication and test equipment. It has a simple twist and pull bayonet action for release, which makes it a lot quicker to change over than the PL259. Unfortunately, its smaller dimensions make it more fiddly to attach to the cable. It is difficult to give specific instructions on fitting as construction differs greatly between makes of plugs.

SMA

This is a miniature connector that has been introduced for use on some very small types of portable radio equipment. It's a screw type, almost like a very small PL-259. I would advise against trying to fit your own coax directly to a mating plug – it's a lot easier to instead use an SMA to BNC adapter which you should find is available from any radio dealer who supplies SMA-equipped receivers to hobbyist users.

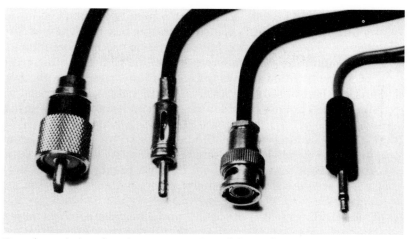

Typical aerial plugs found on scanners. From left to right: PL259, Motorola, BNC and miniature jack. The latter is usually confined to handheld sets.

Motorola type

This is the car radio aerial type of plug that will be familiar to people who have installed or replaced their car radio at some time. Surprisingly in a way, this low quality type of plug (low quality in terms of performance at VHF and UHF) was found on several very early scanners including the SX200N and some early Bearcats. Types vary with manufacturer, but a look at the plug will usually make it clear how it is attached to the cable.

Miniature jack

A plug that is far from suited to VHF/UHF but it is occasionally found on some of the smaller portable crystal-controlled scanners: probably chosen because it is small and very cheap. A look inside will make it obvious as to what is soldered to where, but a difficulty arises in that most miniature jack plugs do not have a big enough opening in the barrel to take 50 ohm coaxial cable. One way round this problem is to cut off the back end of the barrel with say, a hacksaw, so leaving a bigger opening.

MOUNTING EXTERNAL AERIALS

A whole range of fittings and mounting kits is available for installing aerials – your local TV aerial erection firm should be only too happy to sell you poles, fixing kits, etc., and dealers such as Maplin can also supply a range of fixings. There are four basic ways of mounting an aerial outside and the corresponding kits are:

(1) Wall mounting   This consists of a plate with brackets to hold a mounting pole. A drill capable of drilling into brick or masonry will be needed and expanding bolts should be used to retain the plate.

(2) Eaves mounting   A smaller version of the wall-mounting version, it is used with wood screws to fix onto the eaves. Note, though, that this method is only suitable for small lightweight aerials: even a small aerial can put considerable strain on its mountings during high winds.

(3) Chimney lashing   The method often used for TV aerials, comprising one or two brackets held to a chimney by wire cable. Although easy to fit, it places the aerial in close proximity to the heat and smoke from the chimney which may accelerate the inevitable corrosion of the aerial.

(4) Free-standing mast   This is the most expensive solution but usually the best if you can afford it. An aluminium mast of 6 metres or more in length is partially sunk into the ground and held upright with wire guys. This mounting method can improve performance remarkably at some locations as it allows the aerial to be sited away from obstructions and above the level of trees and buildings that block signals. Planning permission is usually required for this kind of installation.

AERIAL AMPLIFIERS

Also known as RF or wideband preamps, signal boosters, etc., these devices fall into two categories:

Masthead amplifiers

These units consist of a small-signal amplifier housed in a weatherproof box, physically close to the aerial and usually mounted at, or very close to, the aerial connection point. They are useful for making up for the signal losses that occur when long cables are used between the aerial and the scanner. DC voltage to power the unit is fed up the centre core of the coaxial cable – as the signal comes down, the DC goes up, without interference. One variant on this theme is a broadband aerial that actually has an aerial amplifier built into its base.

Cable-end amplifiers

These connect between the end of the cable and the scanner. They are often powered by a small battery, although some do plug into the domes-

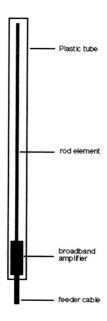

Plastic tube

rod element

broadband
amplifier

feeder cable

Figure 4.7 The active whip for base use.

tic AC supply. Cable-end amplifiers have limitations as, unlike masthead amplifiers, they cannot improve a poor signal-to-noise ratio of an aerial system.

When to use an amplifier

In ideal circumstances, i.e. with an aerial of sufficient quality and short enough cable, an aerial amplifier is not needed. While capable of boosting weaker signals an aerial amplifier can also cause problems. For instance, strong signals received on other frequencies are also boosted and may overload the scanner. However, some scanner users may live in areas where they are screened by high buildings or land, or may not be able to fit an aerial of sufficiently high quality. In such circumstances an amplifier could help. It may also be of use where long cable runs are necessary between the scanner and the aerial. As a caution, users are advised to seek expert advice before installing an aerial amplifier, as wrongly doing so will cause more problems than it solves.

BLOCKING AND IMAGE PROBLEMS

Whenever you use your scanner, especially with a well-sited aerial connected, you may experience problems from other strong signals in your area. One of these is 'blocking', where the sheer strength of the other signals overloads your receiver and causes the wanted signal to either disappear into the noise or be taken over by the unwanted stronger signal. The other is what is called 'image' reception, where another signal which is a given frequency offset away comes through on the IF 'image' of your scanner. To explain this, if you have a scanner using the common 1st IF of 10.7 MHz, then the image frequency of the main ACARS frequency, 131.725 MHz, is twice 10.7 MHz, i.e. 21.4 MHz, above this, on 153.125 MHz. Unfortunately this is smack bang in the middle of the VHF paging band, where a strong transmission on this frequency could easily swamp

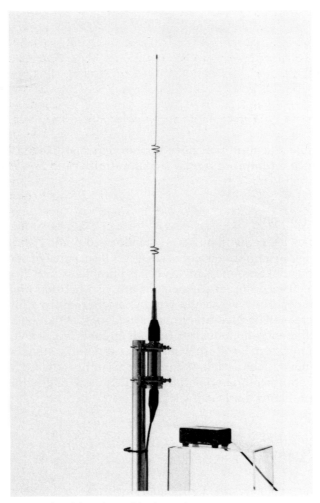

A typical wideband amplified aerial.

the wanted ACARS signals. To overcome this, you can add a suitable filter in line with the coax antenna connection to your scanner (Garex Electronics market a useful tuneable type). In the case of VHF airband, you could try an in-line filter such as the AOR ABF125, available from AOR (UK). This is a purpose-designed airband range 'bandpass' filter, which attenuates signals outside of its range. If it's just a specific frequency you want to attenuate then a simple home-made coaxial stub filter is another option. I've used these on numerous occasions in the past, the arrangement being of a coax stub connected in a T formation with the coax down-lead to your receiver. The stub needs to be a precise electrical quarter wavelength at the frequency you want to attenuate, taking into consideration the velocity factor of the coax used for the stub. For both RG213/UR67M (the thick type approx 10mm diameter, often used for down-leads) and for RG58 and UR76 (the thinner types, around 5mm diameter) the velocity factor will be 0.66. The overall length of the stub in mm will be 75,000 divided by the frequency, multiplied overall by the velocity factor. So, in the case of coax types above, the length in mm will be 49,500 divided by the frequency in MHz, and at 153.125 MHz you'll need a stub length of 323mm. In practice, the velocity factor can vary very slightly between batches of coax, and your T termination will also have some effect, so I would suggest making the length about 20mm longer and carefully cutting off, say, 2mm at a time for maximum attenuation of the unwanted signal. The end of the stub should be open circuit, i.e., with the inner conductor and outer braid not touching each other. You can either use a BNC T-piece with BNC connectors at each coax end, or just solder the inners and outers together directly. At these low VHF frequencies, even one of the small versions of 'chocolate block' connectors could be pressed into service at a pinch.

5 Radio systems explained

After you have started out, have you ever wondered why you can sometimes hear part of a conversation, while on some systems conversations seem to appear and disappear in mid-conversation? Also, what are those strange tones and other signals heard on the bands? Hopefully this chapter will be of use to explain at least some of what you hear.

SINGLE FREQUENCY SIMPLEX

This is when the radio communication you're listening to takes place on one frequency, let's say 145.550 MHz. Station A has his say, then releases his microphone push-to-talk to let station B reply. Station B uses the same frequency to transmit on as station A, and if station C wants to join in, then providing he's in range of both all he has to do is 'butt in' between transmissions. Typical examples are aircraft communication and CB operation. This is all nice and simple, so why can't it all be like this? Surely for push-to-talk communication it would make sense for each user just to use a given frequency for this?

DUAL FREQUENCY SIMPLEX

This is where one user transmits on one frequency, the other on a different frequency, with their corresponding receiver set accordingly. You would think that with the shortage of frequencies (some of the bands are getting very congested) this is rather a waste of a valuable resource – the radio spectrum. But it's not always that simple.

Take the case of a PMR (Private Mobile Radio) service. The base station aerial is often well sited, communicating with mobile and portable stations with their (normally) lower power transmitters and aerials at ground level. Here, the base station would typically transmit on one frequency and receive in the same band but on a different frequency, with the mobiles/portables operating on the reverse of these. The communications range of a base station to another base station sharing the same frequency would be fairly large, but not for the mobiles/portables, which often only need to communicate with their own base. So, with a bit of careful planning of frequencies by individual countries' licensing bodies, taking hills and so on into account, better frequency re-use can be achieved than with a simplex system.

You may sometimes happen upon a transmission on one half of such a system, apparently communicating with someone else you know you should be able to receive. In this case, you now know you need to look for the other half on a different frequency.

TALKTHROUGH

But what happens when two mobiles want to communicate with each other? As they transmit and receive on different frequencies, this would be rather difficult without external help. This comes in the form of the base station which has radio frequency filtering circuits added to allow simultaneous transmission and reception on its separate frequencies. With its receiver audio linked to the transmitter audio, this allows it to relay the signals received on its well-located aerial system, using the higher power base transmitter and the same well-located aerial. This is commonly called, quite simply, a 'repeater'.

This can allow users to communicate even when there's no operator present at the base station desk, such as out of office hours. If a night watchman for example is issued with a portable radio, he can use the repeater to communicate with other employees who are also 'on the radio'. At other times, the base station control operator can switch talkthrough on and off depending on operational requirements, thus explaining why you can sometimes hear both sides of the conversations, and sometimes not. Again, you may happen to stumble on the input frequency of such a system, with users apparently communicating with each other – in this case you'll need to look for the output frequency.

COMMUNITY REPEATERS

A well-sited repeater system doesn't need to be restricted to a single user. Many PMR users only require short periods of communication throughout the day, so a better use of such a valuable resource is often shared among several different groups of users, with the base station operator of each simply having a radio transceiver on the same transmit/receive frequencies as the mobile and portable units, the repeater relaying the audio of all these. To prevent disturbance and maintain a degree of privacy between groups of users, CTCSS (Continuous Tone Controlled Squelch System) is commonly used. Here, the transmitters of each group automatically radiate a low sub-audible CTCSS tone, typically between 67 Hz and 250 Hz in audio frequency, along with their speech, which the repeater regenerates. The accompanying receivers have decoder circuits fitted which only enable the receiver audio when the correct tone is present, keeping it quiet otherwise (i.e., when no signal, or a signal with a different tone, is received). To prevent interference between users, each user's transmitter circuit is disabled if the receiver senses an incorrect tone, preventing one user from accidentally transmitting on top of another.

Many such repeater systems are in use, and although a casual monitoring check may reveal several different users, they're all communicating in relative privacy from each other.

INTERCONNECTION

A community repeater is fine for communication in a given area, but what about users who want communication over a larger area, one which can only be given by a number of such base station sites? One way is to have a number of simultaneously interconnected base stations, all operating on the same frequency (these actually operate with a carefully controlled few Hz difference in frequency between them). Here the mobile user's transceiver stays on a given channel, and the base station's messages (and the relayed talkthrough audio from other mobiles/portables) is transmitted over all the base stations simultaneously. The few Hz difference involved in this quasi-synchronous system can sometimes be heard as a semi-rapid fading in the received signal if the receiver is stationary – this effect all but disappears when the user becomes 'mobile'.

TRUNKING

An alternative method, making use of 'intelligent' multi-channel radios operating under microprocessor control, makes use of a technique called trunking. Here, multi-channel two-frequency base stations are sited at strategic points in the required coverage area, each covering an individu-

Directional aerials used for the lineside trunked radio
system used on the UK's railways.

ally defined area cell. They transmit a continuous system control data
stream on one of their operating channels, with several other channels at
each base station being used as needed for actual communication. The
mobile set automatically searches out this system channel for the area it's
in and locks onto it, automatically sending a short 'I'm here' data signal to
the base station giving the mobile's identity. When a call comes in, the
system channel sends out a data sequence to the mobile, typically
instructing it to automatically shift its channel to one of the communication channels in use at that base station, where communication takes
place. Each base station is linked to the other, so conversations can take
place between sites, or of course in the case of cellular telephony also
between a landline system and the radio network. As the mobile unit
travels around, its channel can be automatically controlled by the base

stations to move to that of a neighbouring site - this often happens without the user realising he's being 'handed off' between base station cells.

The use of trunking isn't new – it's been used on landlines and also for STD (Subscriber Trunk Dialling) for many years. Its use in radio systems however is increasing every day, as it's an efficient means of using a limited number of communications channels. Trunking dynamically allocates a radio channel, usually a two-frequency channel with each end transmitting and receiving on different frequencies, and with at least the base end operating in full-duplex mode.

Trunked radio systems operate in a similar way to telephone trunking. Here, a given number of lines are available, between two cities for example, with a much larger total number of users who have access to these lines. Not all users wish to have communication at the same time, so the lines are allocated as and when needed, for the exclusive use of that call but only for as long as it's needed. Radio trunking is basically the same, where a given number of radio channels in each area are shared between a large number of radio users, the radio units having built-in circuitry to automatically change channel as and when needed. In other words, they're intelligent radio units. A pool of radio channels is available which is used as and when needed by each radio, after which the channel is returned to the common pool.

One example of a trunked system is cellular radio telephony, another is the UK Band III network, and some community repeater systems are operating with multi-channel trunking. Here's how it works:

Multi-channel

For each base station, a number of radio channels are used, normally with the rack of transmitter/receivers combined into a common aerial system or systems. One of the channels for each coverage area is known as a control channel – this usually sends out a constant stream of data giving registration and call information. Some PMR systems may cycle this channel between the other channels, or indeed time-share it with control channels at other base station sites in the same system.

When a mobile radio unit is switched on, it first hunts and locks onto this control channel. It first checks that it is the correct system etc. that the mobile is registered for, if not then it hunts for another control channel from its pre-stored list of frequencies. Once it has confirmed this, it sends a short burst of registration data to the system, to say 'I'm switched on and available for communication at this site'. This is done on the reverse control channel, i.e., the split frequency that the radio system is listening on. The trunking system controller updates itself with that information, to the effect that such-and-such a mobile identity is logged on to that base.

Calling

When the radio user places a call, the mobile again transmits a short burst of data to the system, on the reverse control channel. If a speech communication channel is available, the system, again via the control channel, instructs that mobile to automatically shift frequency to the allocated channel which is used until the end of that period of communication. After the end of the communication, the mobile reverts back to silently monitoring the control channel, and the communication channel which was used is placed back into the pool of available channels for all users.

Cellular coverage

Because of the multi-frequency availability by both base stations and mobile radios, combined with carefully tailored coverage areas for each base station transmitter site using VHF and UHF frequencies, the same frequencies can be reused a given distance away. By adding coverage areas in this way, a network based on cellular coverage areas can be achieved, with overlaps between cells to ensure that mobiles moving in between these cells can always achieve communication on one channel or another. Neighbouring cell sites must of course use different frequencies for the control channel, plus different frequencies for the communication channels, to avoid problems to mobile stations at overlapping signal areas.

Automatic hand-off

When a mobile moves from one cell coverage area into the next, the signal strength from the first control channel, which the mobile is silently monitoring, gets progressively weaker. At a given level, the set's 'brain' decides 'this is too weak, I'll try to find another' and commences to scan the frequencies in its internal memory to try to find a stronger control channel. When it does, it again re-registers with a data burst on the reverse control channel to update the system as to its location. Any incoming calls to that mobile will then be routed to that site rather than the site it was last registered on.

When the mobile radio user is in the middle of a conversation, and starts running out of coverage of the first cell and into that of another, an automatic hand-off can occur. Here another data burst automatically instructs the set to shift frequency to that of a given communication channel allocated for its use on the neighbouring site.

Monitoring

When scanning across a given frequency range used by a trunked system in situations where you are allowed to monitor such things, you'll typically hear a channel constantly transmitting a high-pitched warble, 24 hours a day. This is the control channel, and if you listen carefully you may hear slight changes, this being the data transmitted as calls are made and the like. A number of communication channels are associated with each control channel and when these are in use at any given time you'll hear normal speech possibly combined with data bursts as the mobiles are instructed to change power and so on, and finally a burst followed by the signal dropping in mid-conversation when the mobile is either instructed to move frequency onto a channel on the next site or when the call has been completed. The channels used are invariably split frequency, i.e., mobiles transmit on one frequency and receive on another. Some are half-duplex, i.e., push-to-talk where only one side of the conversation is normally heard if communication is being made between different sites.

TETRA

TETRA is TErrestrial Trunked RAdio, which is a digital radio system eminently suitable for emergency services. It gives high speech quality in noisy conditions and full duplex speech, as well as text and even slow-scan digitised video transmission capabilities. It operates on 380–400 MHz across Europe, with the facility for up to 4 communication channels on each radio channel frequency. Radios can also have features such as a panic button and even automatic position finding. The aim is that all police forces in England, Scotland and Wales will have the system available by the year 2003, the plan being that all UK emergency services will use TETRA by 2008 in the 380–400 MHz band. There is also a planned civil TETRA system in the UK operating on 410.0–415.0 MHz (mobile transmit) and 420.0–425.0 MHz (base transmit), both sub-bands being shared with government services.

SPEECH ENCRYPTION

Many services naturally want to keep their on-air conversations private, usually not primarily from scanner enthusiasts who just listen in for a hobby but from others who could use the information to their advantage. Typical cases could be a taxi firm with other firms poaching their business, as well as both private and government security services such as store detectives and the police.

Digital communication, using services such as TETRA or GSM cell-phones are one answer of course, and TETRA has a high level of built-in encryption available for governmental use. Digital scrambling is also possible on normal PMR channels, although this is not commonly allowed in the UK for non-governmental purposes over a wide coverage area, but simple types of scrambling are currently allowed for on-site PMR use, e.g. security guards using portable to portable communication with hand-helds, or for hospital and prison safety communication. A typical type of digital scrambling is the MASC system, where the audio is digitised and encrypted before transmission, then digitally unencrypted and converted back to audio at the receiver. The resultant transmitted audio, due to the pseudo-random nature of the digital transmission, often sound just like noise on a normal receiver.

Analogue forms of encryption are less secure, but usually have the advantage of being small circuits with much lower current consumption than their digital counterparts, making the overall portable radio smaller and lighter to carry around. 'Add-on' analogue scramblers for retrofitting in normal radios are also available. Some of these use a rolling-code technique, which can be identified by periodic bursts of synchronising data pulses along with the scrambled speech. Others, even simpler, use what is known as frequency inversion, and this system is fitted to at least one type of widely-available PMR handheld. Here, the user's speech is simply inverted, with low frequencies coming out as high frequencies and high frequencies coming out as low frequencies. At the receiving end, the reverse simply happens to result in readable audio again. It's interesting to note that some scanners, such as the Yupiteru MVT9000 have a switchable voice inverter incorporated, and a base AOR scanner, as well as their AR-8200, can have an optional inverter unit fitted.

CTCSS

CTCSS stands for Continuous Tone Controlled Squelch System, often called Sub Tone because it uses a system in which speech transmission is accompanied by a continuous low-frequency tone, in the range 67 Hz to 250.3 Hz, i.e. lower than the speech range of 300–3000 Hz on a radio system. It's widely used in mobile radio fields, as well as an access method for amateur VHF/UHF repeaters, to give a degree of discrimination between different users on the same channel.

On the air, each user's transmitter generates a given CTCSS frequency, at a low level, along with the speech transmission, and a special decoder is fitted in the receiver to detect only that individual tone. When it does, it opens the receiver squelch, otherwise the speaker remains silent, with

Table 5.1 CTCSS frequencies

67.0Hz	107.2Hz	167.9Hz
71.9Hz	110.9Hz	173.8Hz
74.4Hz	114.8Hz	179.9Hz
77.0Hz	118.8Hz	186.2Hz
79.7Hz	123.0Hz	192.8Hz
82.5Hz	127.3Hz	203.5Hz
85.4Hz	131.8Hz	210.7Hz
88.5Hz	136.5Hz	218.1Hz
91.5Hz	141.3Hz	225.7Hz
94.8Hz	146.2Hz	233.6Hz
97.4Hz	151.4Hz	241.8Hz
100.0Hz	156.7Hz	250.3Hz
103.5Hz	162.2Hz	

the radios of each individual fleet or group of users being fitted with the same tone frequency. This way, a number of different groups of radio users all on the same channel can use that channel without being over-heard by others – that is unless you're listening with an open receiver such as a scanner, when everyone will come through! Often, there's a busy channel lockout fitted in PMR transceivers, so that a given user can-not transmit if their set is receiving a different tone to its own, to prevent it interfering with other stations. A common base station repeater is often shared by a number of different PMR users, each having a different tone, on the basis of time-sharing a valuable resource such as a hilltop-located repeater station, which automatically re-radiates the signals from mobile and portable users from a well-located site. The repeater re-radiates the CTCSS tone as well as the speech, and often also has time-outs fitted for each user group, just like an amateur repeater, to make sure each group gets a fair share of the available airtime.

SELECTIVE SIGNALLING

In many cases on a radio system, an all-informed net where all users hear what's happening on the radio channel is very useful. This is typical in an emergency services environment such as the police where everyone hear-ing all communications on the local channel is advantageous, as other officers could either benefit from this or even offer further information from what they hear. But the need to be able to selectively call an individual radio user, or a group of users, has been a desirable ideal in a number of radio systems, both government and business mobile radio services.

Let's say there's an undercover squad who only want to hear messages intended for them, where a radio bleating out an intruder alarm activation miles away could blow a cover. Also for a council's parks and highways maintenance unit, who would otherwise be distracted by having to listen out for all messages on the channel while they're working away from the vehicle, just in case one of the radio calls was intended for their unit to respond to.

One method of such individual calling is, of course, cellular telephones. These have an airtime charge of a certain cost per call or time of call, but the great limitation of these for the all-informed net – e.g. for emergency services such as the police, ambulance, or security officers on a factory site – is that there is no facility whatsoever for group calling. i.e., a call to several people such as 3, 6 or whatever, all at the same time.

Being able to individually call a specific mobile or portable radio unit, or a defined group of these, can thus be of benefit. For example, "Any ambulance able to attend a two-person injury RTA southbound M1 Junction 12" is useful in an all-informed net, but a specific call would be beneficial if a subsequent call is needed to the specific ambulance for an update of its arrival at the casualty unit, when the crew would be otherwise engaged in attending to the injured person and negotiating traffic and where general radio traffic might become a background intrusion.

5-TONE

Across the PMR communications spectrum, many radio transmissions can be heard being preceded by a short musical toneburst sequence, of around a half second to a second in duration. This is sequential tone signalling, more commonly referred to as 5-tone from the usual number of individual tones used for each sequence. Here, each mobile radio is allocated a unique 5-digit ID, which a decoder in each radio is equipped to automatically respond to. When the base station dispatcher wishes to call an individual radio user, they enter the radio's ID onto a 5-tone keypad or a PC-based dispatcher-based system, and the transmitter automatically fires up with the tone sequence according to the entered ID.

When the transmitted tone sequence matches the one stored in the receiving radio, it opens the audio path to the speaker so the user can hear the dispatcher's call. Otherwise it remains silent with the user being blissfully unaware of all the other radio activity happening on that channel.

Sometimes the mobile radios in a given system are equipped to automatically transmit their own 5-digit ID each time the user presses the radio PTT (push-to-talk), to automatically identify themselves to the dispatcher. A variation to this is a status transmission, where the mobile user can manually change the final digit between 0 and 9, or the final two digits (e.g. 00–99) of their transmitted 5-tone ID, according to their status, so 0 could indicate off duty, 1 on duty, 2 at customer's premises, 3 awaiting a new job and so on. In the case of a two-digit status one of the digits could typically be used indicate the general location area of the mobile at a given time. The first three or four fixed digits of the 5-tone sequence are thus the mobile's individual ID, the final one or two manually variable digits being their status at any time.

With such mobile status facilities, the dispatcher often is able to automatically interrogate the mobile with a 5-tone call to that mobile, where on receipt it will automatically transpond with its ID and the status that has been set by the user. This way the dispatcher can see if a radio user is available for a job or not, without the need for a voice call.

It can also work the other way, where in a busy radio system all that a user needs to do is select their status and press a button on the radio to manually transmit this. So, when signing on in the morning or after a lunch break, the radio user only needs to transmit a short burst of 5-tone rather than a longer speech transmission to say they're in the vehicle and either available for work (e.g. in the case of a taxi) or on their way to their first job.

Another use is that of an panic facility, where each radio is also programmed with a unique 5-tone emergency ID that is transmitted if the vehicle driver hits a panic button on the dashboard. This automatically transmits the mobile's emergency status, possibly followed by a 10 or 20 seconds of live microphone so the driver can call for help over the radio system without the need to fumble about with radio controls.

DTMF

Some PMR equipments use DTMF signalling (Dual Tone Medium Frequency, as used for telephone dialling) rather than single-tone frequency signalling. This typically uses a string of three digits for each radio ID, although radio-to-radio selective calling can use six digits, the first three being the called party and the last three the calling party, to display on the called radio who's calling. Each digit is made up of an audio tone pair, and there are plenty of decoders readily available to decode and display these sequences, even shareware PC programs which use your sound card as the audio-to-PC interface.

ACARS

If you're an airband enthusiast, then you may have heard of ACARS, the Aircraft Control and Reporting System. This is an automatic data system used by civil airlines around the world, to transmit real-time data of flight status reports together with data and text messages involving both passengers and crew. Time of 'wheels-up', touchdown, plus ground and air speed are typical transmissions, along with text-based information such as schedules, weather information, status messages from the aircraft such as engine performance, fuel usage, emergency conditions and even exact times of takeoff, passenger door openings and so on. Other messages can include private or company messages either between airline staff or for passengers on the craft.

To decode the data, all you need is a suitable interface and decoding program, of which there are a number commercially available such as the Lowe Airmaster. Alternatively, you can use the sound card of your PC as the data interface, running a program such as WACARS, i.e. Windows ACARS. The main frequency used in Europe is 131.725 MHz, where you'll often hear periodic data bursts from a number of aircraft. AOR also produce a portable self-contained ACARS decoder for out-and-about use.

An ACARS transmission sounds like a short high-frequency (2400 Hz) audio burst, followed by a data stream which sound very much like an amateur packet radio transmission, i.e. a raspy noise lasting between a half second and several seconds, depending upon the length of the data being sent.

PAGING

Personal digital and alphanumeric pagers are widely used, and many listeners will have heard the 'Brrrrrrr...brrppppp' paging signals on VHF and UHF (see Chapter 6 *UK frequency allocations*), which are high-powered paging transmitters sending text messages out to predefined users.

The system widely used for this is called POCSAG, which stands for Post Office Code Standardisation Advisory Group, and there is a very easy, and freely available, way of decoding these messages. You just use appropriate freeware or shareware software running on a PC, together with a either a simple interface between your receiver and the PC's serial port – some decoders can alternatively use a PC sound card as the interface.

As POCSAG is transmitted as direct FSK, the best way is to take the data direct from the receiver's internal discriminator circuit, rather than from the earphone or external speaker connector, although some base scanners such as the Icom PCR-1000 have a dedicated data output facility.

Incidentally, because VHF pagers use small, internal aerials, the paging transmitters are usually very high-powered affairs in order to give blanket coverage. Unfortunately, because of the proximity of the paging allocations to other frequencies, scanner users often have problems (sometimes very severe) with interference from the unwanted pager base transmissions. This is where the technical results in the *Scanners and accessories review* section of this book on real scanner performance become invaluable, as you can see which sets have better blocking rejection than others before you go out and spend your hard-earned cash!

6 UK frequency allocations

The decision on who transmits what, on which frequency, is made by international agreement. Clearly, governments must agree on allocations if they are to avoid causing interference. There would be chaos if, say, one country allocated a band to low powered radio telephones while a neighbouring country allocated the same band for high powered broadcasting. The body which co-ordinates radio frequency allocations on behalf of world governments is the International Telecommunications Union, known simply as the ITU. For the purpose of agreed allocations the ITU splits the world into three regions. The United Kingdom falls in Region 1, which includes most of Europe and a small section of North Africa. However, it does not necessarily follow that each country conforms strictly with the allocations drawn up for that region. Where there is little likelihood of interference, countries may opt for local variations and, obviously, many such variations exist. For this reason, listings given in this book strictly apply only to the United Kingdom, although most allocations do match the standard format for Region 1. We shall look first at general VHF/UHF frequency allocations, then consider in detail some of the services on those allocations. Table 6.1 is a listing of UK frequency allocations.

Table 6.1 United Kingdom frequency allocations

From-to	Pairing	Allocation
25.0050–25.0100		Standard frequency, time signals, space research
25.0100–25.0700		Fixed (PTO & government), maritime & land mobile (government)
25.0700–25.2100		Maritime mobile (mostly USB and RTTY)
25.0539	26.1444	Ship-to-shore (SSB)
25.0601	26.1506	Ship-to-shore (SSB)
25.0710		Marine calling channel A
25.0730		Marine calling channel B
25.0750		Marine calling channel C
25.0763 to 25.0898		Marine channels spaced 0.5 kHz

From-to	Pairing	Allocation
25.2100–25.6000		Fixed (PTO & government), maritime & land mobile (government)
25.2100 to 25.5350		Worldwide coastal stations
25.5500 to 25.6000		Radio astronomy
25.6000–26.1000		Broadcasting (AM) plus radio astronomy
26.1000–27.5000		Fixed (PTO & government), land mobile (including CEPT CB system), pagers, ISM, maritime mobile, model control
26.1000	26.1750	MOD tactical land mobile
26.1444	25.0539	Shore-to-ship (SSB)
26.1506	25.0601	Shore-to-ship (SSB)
26.2375 to 26.8655		One-way paging systems (new band)
26.9780 to 27.2620		One-way paging systems (old band)
26.9570 to 27.2830		Industrial, scientific and medical
26.9600 to 27.2800		Model control (AM & FM & 1.5 watt maximum power) & data buoys
26.9650 to 27.4050		CEPT Citizens Band radio (mostly NFM but some AM & SSB)
27.4500		Emergency alarm systems for the elderly or infirmed
27.5000–27.6000		Land mobile (government) meteorological aids (sondes etc.)
27.6000–28.0000		Land mobile (UK CB system) & meteorological aids
27.60125 to 27.99125		UK Citizens Band radio system (NFM)
28.0000–29.7000		Amateur radio (10 metre band) including Russian RS-series satellites, also licence-exempt short range devices
29.7000–30.7000		Space (satellite identification), mobile (government) & fixed
29.7000 to 29.9700		Military 25 kHz channel spacing simplex communications
29.7000 to 30.0100		Satellite identification
30.0250 to 30.7000		USAF (Europe) mobile communications 25 kHz channels
30.4500		US Military MARS radio integration network
30.700–34.5000		Fixed, mobile & paging systems (at the peak of 11 year sunspot cycles many US services operating in this band can be heard)
30.7000 to 34.5000		Use by USAF in UK/Europe and MOD. Mostly NFM at 25 kHz channel spacing
31.0375	39.9375	CT1 cordless phones base unit Tx
31.0625	39.9625	CT1 cordless phones base unit Tx
31.0875	39.9875	CT1 cordless phones base unit Tx
31.1125	40.0125	CT1 cordless phones base unit Tx
31.1375	40.0375	CT1 cordless phones base unit Tx
31.1625	40.0625	CT1 cordless phones base unit Tx
31.1875	40.0875	CT1 cordless phones base unit Tx
31.2125	40.1125	CT1 cordless phones base unit Tx
31.7250		Hospital paging systems
31.7500		Hospital paging systems
31.7750		Hospital paging systems
31.8000 to 34.9000		Military fixed/mobile 50 kHz channel spacing
34.5000–37.5000		Mobile (mostly government & military), model control, alarms
34.9250		Emergency alarm systems for the aged and infirmed
34.9500		Emergency alarm systems for the aged and infirmed
34.9750		Emergency alarm systems for the aged and infirmed
35.0050 to 35.2050		Model control (aircraft only) 1.5 watt maximum power
35.2500 to 37.7500		Military (mostly army) fixed/mobile 50 kHz channel spacing

From-to	Pairing	Allocation
37.5000–47.0000		Mobile (extensively military vehicles and manpacks), radio astronomy, ISM, cordless telephones, television broadcasting & model control
37.7500 to 38.2500		Cambridge Observatory (astronomy)
37.7500 to 40.0000		Military mobile 50 kHz channel spacing
39.9150 to 40.1200		Some beacons on space satellites have used this sub-band
39.9375	31.0375	CT1 cordless phones portable unit Tx
39.9625	31.0625	CT1 cordless phones portable unit Tx
39.9875	31.0875	CT1 cordless phones portable unit Tx
40.0125	31.1125	CT1 cordless phones portable unit Tx
40.0375	31.1375	CT1 cordless phones portable unit Tx
40.0625	31.1625	CT1 cordless phones portable unit Tx
40.0875	31.1875	CT1 cordless phones portable unit Tx
40.1125	31.2125	CT1 cordless phones portable unit Tx
40.0500		***Military distress frequency***
40.6650 to 40.9550		Model control (100m watt maximum)
40.6800		Industrial, scientific & medical
41.0000 to 47.4500		Military tactical mobile (vehicles/manpacks/data) 50 kHz channel
41.000 to 68.0000		Television broadcasting (not UK) Band I
46.6100 to 46.9700		Unapproved cordless telephone handsets (US system B & NFM)
47.309375		Long-range security alarms
47.318750		Long-range security alarms
47.331250		Long-range security alarms
47.356250		Long-range security alarms
47.4000		Vehicle paging alarms
47.41875	77.5500	Extended range CT1
47.43125	77.5125	Cordless phones
47.45625 to 47.54375	1.6240 to 1.7829	Cordless telephone handsets (approved & 8 channels NFM)
47.6800–50.0000		Land mobile, broadcasting, amateur & baby listeners, walkie-talkies, wireless microphones & cordless phones (all NFM)
48.9750		On-site radio paging
48.9875		On-site radio paging
48.9900 to 49.6800	69.7200 to 70.2750	Unapproved long range cordless phone bases (22 channels NFM)
49.0000 to 49.8750		Private paging systems
49.0000 to 50.0000		Unapproved devices mostly intended for use in USA
49.4250 to 49.4750		Hospital paging systems
49.6700 to 49.9700		Unapproved cordless telephone bases (US system B NFM)
49.8200 to 49.9000		Low-powered radio control toys, baby alarms, walkie-talkies etc. (100m watt max power)
49.8300 to 49.8900		Unapproved cordless telephones
50.0000–54.0000		6 metre amateur band (US allocation & NFM, CW SSB)
50.0000 to 52.0000		6 metre amateur band (UK allocation & NFM, CW & SSB)
54.0000		Frequency has been used by space satellite beacons (Anna-1B)
50.5000		Video transmissions, railways track to train using leaky feeder
52.0000–60.0000		Land mobile and radio microphones
53.8000 to 55.6000		BBC high-powered (4 watt) radio microphones
60.0000–64.0000		Radio microphones
60.8000 to 62.6000		BBC radio microphones, 100 kHz channel spacing
64.0000–68.0000		Fixed & land mobile including military
64.0000 to 68.0000		MOD Pegasus-MOULD system, 12.5 kHz channel spacing

From-to	Pairing	Allocation
68.0000–70.0250		Land mobile & repeaters (military)
69.3000		Spot frequency for Sea Cadets (AM)
69.6000 to 69.8000	84.6000 to 84.8000	Military repeater outputs
69.8250 to 69.9750		Outside broadcast camera links (talkback)
70.0000 to 70.0500		Unapproved cordless phones
70.0250–70.5000		4 metre amateur band, CW, NFM and SSB in use
70.5000–71.5000		Land mobile (emergency services)
70.5125 to 84.0000	80.0000 to 71.5000	Fire service bases
71.5000–72.8000		Low band PMR mobiles (bases + 13.5 MHz)
71.5125 to 72.7875	85.0125 to 86.2875	Extensively used by water boards, telecoms & local authorities using both AM and NFM
71.9875		Automobile Association Ch 6 (London)
72.0000		Automobile Association ('Fanum') Ch 7
72.0125		Automobile Association Ch 4
72.0205		Automobile Association Ch 1
72.0500		Automobile Association Ch 3
72.0625		Automobile Association Ch 2
72.0875		Automobile Association Ch 5
72.3750	85.8750	Short-term hire mobile
72.5250 to 72.7000	86.0250 to 86.2000	Ambulance bases in some areas
72.5375	86.0375	Private ambulances national network (mobiles)
72.8000–74.8000		Land mobile (government)
72.8000 to 73.7000		Military simplex channels using 25 kHz spacing
73.7000 to 74.7875		Military (RAF ground services) & MOULD repeater inputs
74.8000–75.2000		Aeronavigation guard band
75.0000		Approach fan beams, inner, middle & outer markers (AM)
75.2000–76.7000		Outside broadcast links and military & mostly allocated to USAF British bases (NFM) and MOULD repeater outputs
75.20000 to 75.30000		BBC outside broadcast links
75.30000 to 76.50000		Military MOULD repeater outputs
76.7000–78.0000		Fixed and land mobile (PMR and government)
76.9625 to 77.5000	86.9625 to 87.5000	Fixed and mobile, government, Customs, British Telecom, RAC and PMR mobiles
77.0000	87.0000	RAC Ch 2
77.0125	87.0125	RAC Ch 4
77.0250	87.0250	RAC Ch 1
77.0375	87.0375	RAC Ch 5
77.0500	87.0500	RAC Ch 3
77.5125	47.43125	Extended range CT1
77.5500	47.41875	Cordless phones
78.0000–80.0000		Land mobile, government and private users.
78.1000		Air Training Corps (nationwide)
78.1875		BBC OB and engineering
78.2000		BBC OB and engineering
78.2125		Microwave link setting-up channel (nationwide) and BBC OB crews
78.2225		BBC OB and engineering
78.2375		BBC OB and engineering
78.2500		BBC OB and engineering
79.0000 to 80.0000		MOULD repeater inputs and RAF ground services/police

From-to	Pairing	Allocation
80.0000–84.0000		Land mobile & fixed (extensive emergency service use)
80.5000 to 82.5000		Radio astronomy (Cambridge University)
80.0000 to 84.0000	70.5000 to 71.5000	Fire mobiles
80.0125		Fire tender intercommunication (Channel 21)
80.0750		Fire tender intercommunication (Channel 22)
81.9500		Fire operations London
83.9960 to 84.0040		ISM
84.0000–85.0000		**Fixed & land mobile (mostly military)**
84.1250 to 84.3500	73.7000 to 73.9250	RAF ground service bases
84.3000		RAF Mountain rescue teams (single frequency simplex)
84.0000 to 85.0000		Military repeater inputs
85.0000–87.5000		Low band PMR bases
85.125 to 86.2875	71.5125 to 72.7825	Extensively used by water boards, telecoms, local authorities & using both AM and NFM
85.1375 to 85.2000		Numerous British Telecom engineering channels
85.4875		Automobile Association bases Ch 6
85.5000		Automobile Association bases Ch 7
85.5125		Automobile Association bases Ch 4
85.5250		Automobile Association bases Ch 1
85.5500		Automobile Association bases Ch 3
85.5625		Automobile Association bases Ch 2
85.5875		Automobile Association bases Ch 5
85.8500	72.2500	National engineering channel
85.8750	72.3750	Low band demonstration and short-term hire channel bases
86.0375	72.5375	Private ambulance bases (national network)
86.1375	72.6375	National engineering channel
86.2000	72.7000	Automobile Association
86.3000 to 86.7000		Single frequency simplex channels (channels listed below are in use in many parts of Britain but may vary in some areas)
86.3125		National Mountain Rescue channel 1
86.3250		St John Ambulance/Red Cross channel 1
86.3500		National Mountain Rescue channel 2 (in some areas, Red Cross, St John Ambulance, REACT and lifeguards)
86.3625		Scouts national channel 1
86.3750		REACT emergency teams (nationwide)
86.4125		St John Ambulance/Red Cross/mountain rescue channel 2
86.4250		Forestry Commission channel 3
86.4375		Motor rally safety channel
86.4500		Forestry Commission channel 2
86.4625		County councils
86.4750		British Rail National Incident channel
86.5000		Nuclear Spills Teams channel 1
86.5250		Nuclear Spills Teams channel 2
86.5500		Nuclear Spills Teams channel 3
86.5750		NCB mine rescue teams
86.6250		Scouts national channel 2
86.6750		Nuclear fire and radiation check teams
86.7000		BNF nuclear hazard check teams
86.9625 to 87.5000	76.9625 to 77.5000	Split frequency simplex bases including some Customs channels and local authorities

From-to	Pairing	Allocation
87.0000	77.0000	RAC Ch 2
87.0125	77.0125	RAC Ch 4
87.0250	77.0250	RAC Ch 1
87.0375	77.0375	RAC Ch 5
87.0500	77.0500	RAC Ch 3
87.5000–108.0000		FM broadcast band (Band II)
99.0230		Frequency has been used by Russian satellites (Cosmos 44)
108.0000–117.9750		Aeronautical radionavigation beacons including VHF Omnirange (VOR) and Doppler VOR (DVOR). Beacons identified by a three letter code in CW. Some of those located at or near airfields carry AM voice information on weather/runway/warnings etc. This service is known as Aerodrome Terminal Information Service (ATIS)
118.0500–136.9750		International aeronautical mobile band. This is the VHF band used by all civilian and some military airfields. It is subdivided into 760 channels (25 kHz spacing) and mode is AM, 8.33 kHz channelling is being introduced
118.0000 to 123.0000		Mostly control tower frequencies
121.5000		***International distress frequency***
121.7500		Soyuz manned T-flights to MIR Space Station (non-standard use of this allocation using NFM)
123.0000 to 130.0000		Mostly airways frequencies (some ground & approach control)
123.1000		Search & Rescue (SAR)
130.0000 to 132.0000		Mostly company frequencies (airline crews to ground staff)
132.0000 to 136.0000		Mostly airways
135.5500 to 135.6450		Sub-band was once used for the American ATS series satellites
137.0000–138.0000		Space-to-Earth communications & weather imaging satellites (see satellite sub-section for full details)
138.0750 to 138.1750		Mercury/Racal paging systems
138.0000 to 138.2000		USAF bases in some areas
138.5000 to 139.5000		Mostly gas boards
139.5000 to 140.5000	148.0000 to 149.0000	Mostly electricity boards (new allocation)
140.1825		Electricity line fault teams
140.1875		Electricity line fault teams
140.2000		Electricity line fault teams
140.5000 to 141.0000		Bus companies
140.96875		Short-term hire channel (single frequency simplex)
141.0000–141.9000		Land mobile mostly used by BBC, independent television and radio for outside broadcast links, radio cars, etc. All single frequency simplex using NFM
141.0000 to 141.2000		Mostly ITV
141.2000 to 141.9000		Mostly BBC
141.9000–143.0000		Mobile (government) including, land, air & space satellite communications & military MOULD repeater links (NFM)
142.0000 to 143.0000		Air-to-air and air-to-ground. Sub-band used fairly extensively by military in continental Europe but rarely in UK
142.4000 to 142.6000		Extensively used for Soyuz/Mir (Russian) satellite links (NFM)
142.7200		USAF air-to-air
142.8200		USAF air-to-air

From-to	Pairing	Allocation
143.0000–144.0000		Mobile (government) mobiles (largely AM) coupled with bases at + 9 MHz. Some Russian space satellite traffic all using NFM
143.000 to 144.0000	152.0000 to 153.0000	Police bases
143.1450 to 143.6250		Soyuz/Mir communications
143.6250		Mir main downlink over Europe (very strong when overhead)
144.0000–146.0000		Amateur 2 metre band including satellite allocation. CW, SSB & NFM used
146.0000–148.0000		Land mobile & fixed. Police mobile channels paired with bases on 154–156 MHz and uplinks to hilltop repeaters
146.0000 to 148.0000		Police fixed links (base to hilltop)
146.0 to 148.0000	154.0000 to 156.0000	Police mobiles
147.8000		Used in many areas for Fire Brigade alert pagers
148.0000–149.0000		Fixed and land mobile. Fuel and power industries.
148.56000		NOAA-series satellite telecommand uplink
149.0000–149.9000		Mobile (military). Used particularly by USAF and RAF and MOULD repeaters
149.8500		Common channel at many military bases
149.9000		Air Training Corps nationwide (channel 2)
149.9000–150.0500		Radionavigation by satellite. Doppler shift position fixing using US satellites (TRANSIT) and Russian (COSNAV) paired with 399.9–400.05 MHz
150.0500–152.0000		Radio astronomy and oil slick markers
150.1100 to 150.1850		Slick markers
152.0000–153.0000		Land mobile police bases paired with mobiles at 143–144 MHz
152.0000 to 152.5500		Metropolitan Police M2PM talkthrough
153.0000–153.5000		National and local area radio paging systems
153.5000–154.0000		Land mobile (military) and meterological aids
154.0000–156.0000		Fixed and mobile (emergency services). This band is used extensively for downlinks from hilltop repeaters to base stations
154.0000 to 156.0000	146.0000 to 148.0000	Police bases
156.0000–174.0000		Fixed & mobile (land and marine). The marine VHF service falls within this band which also includes message handling services and mobile telephone systems. All NFM
156.0000		Marine channel 0. Lifeboats and Coastguard
156.0000 to 157.4250		Marine channels single and split frequency, simplex
156.8000		***Marine distress & calling channel 16***
157.4500 to 158.4000		Private marine channels & message handling services
158.4000 to 158.5250		Private and dockside using simplex
158.5375 to 159.9125		Digital Pacnets
159.2500 to 160.5500		Private channels and message handling services and a few PMR channels
160.5500 to 161.0000		Marine channels
161.0000 to 161.1000	459.1000 to 459.5000	Paging systems acknowledge
161.1250 to 161.5000		Private marine channels
161.5000 to 162.0500		Marine channels
162.0500 to 163.0000		Private channels and message handling services
163.0375 to 164.4125		Digital Pacnets
163.9000	159.4000	PMR (not always split)
163.9250	159.4250	PMR (not always split)

From-to	Pairing	Allocation
163.9875		PMR
164.0000		PMR
164.0875		PMR
164.1250		PMR
164.1875		PMR
164.4375 to 165.0375		Private message handling services including paging and telephone patching
165.625 to 168.2500	169.8625 to 173.0500	High band PMR bases. Also extensive use by security/message handling services including nationwide links
166.0000		Soyuz/Mir (Russian) satellite downlinks
166.1000 to 166.6125		Extensively used by ambulances
167.2000	172.2000	High band demonstration & short-term hire channel bases
167.9920 to 168.0080		Industrial, scientific & medical
168.24375–168.30525		PMR simplex channels
168.2875		Local authority alarms spot frequency
168.31215 to 168.8375		Emergency service fixed links
168.84375 to 169.39375		High band PMR simplex channels
168.9375		Local authority alarms spot frequency
168.9750		BBC Engineering
169.0125 to 169.7625		Short-term hire channels (single frequency simplex) all NFM (used extensively during the RAC Rally)
169.4125 to 169.8125		Pan-European paging system (ERMES)
169.81875–169.84375		PMR simplex channels
172.000	167.2000	Short-term hire mobiles, PMR demo channel
170.4500 to 170.8000	165.8500 to 166.0000	Private security firms' mobiles
170.9000 to 171.4250		Ambulance mobiles
173.04375–173.09375		PMR simplex channels
173.1000 to 173.2000		Low-powered devices
173.2000 to 173.3500		Low-powered telemetry and telecontrol
173.3500 to 173.8000		Radio deaf aids, medical and biological telemetry
173.8000 to 175.0000		Radiomicrophones
174.5000–225.0000		Land mobile, fixed, radiolocation & radiomicrophones, television broadcasting (not UK) Band III upwards from 174 MHz falls within the old Band III TV allocation and these frequencies have been released in the UK for land mobile. Most services operate on a trunked system where the mobile is automatically switched from one base station to another
174.0000 to 174.5000		Emergency service fixed links
174.5000 to 176.5000		PMR simplex channels & radiomicrophones
176.5000 to 183.5000	184.5000 to 191.5000	PMR bases
183.5000 to 184.5000		PMR simplex channels
184.5000 to 191.5000	176.5000 to 183.5000	PMR mobiles
191.5000 to 192.5000		PMR simplex channels
192.5000 to 199.5000	200.5000 to 207.5000	PMR (transport industries' mobiles) and trunked networks
196.0000 to 198.0000	204.0000 to 206.000	British Rail
199.5000 to 200.5000		PMR simplex channels
200.5000 to 207.5000	192.5000 to 199.5000	PMR (transport industries) bases and trunked networks
201.4625 to 203.7125	193.4625 to 195.7125	London Transport
207.5000 to 208.5000		PMR simplex channels
208.5000 to 215.5000	216.5000 to 223.5000	PMR bases

From-to	Pairing	Allocation
215.5000 to 216.5000		PMR simplex channels
216.5000 to 223.5000	208.5000 to 215.5000	PMR mobiles
223.5000 to 225.0000		PMR simplex channels
225.0000—328.6000		Aeronautical mobile (military) using AM simplex, ground-to-air, air-to-air, tactical, etc. Some satellite allocations
235.0000 to 273.0000		Extensively used for military satellite downlinks (FleetSatcom West etc)
243.0000		***Military distress frequency*** Life-raft beacons, SARBEs, PIRBs, etc. Frequency monitored by COSPAS/SARSAT satellites
257.8000		Common airfield frequency
259.7000		NASA shuttles (AM voice)
296.8000		NASA shuttles (AM voice particularly used on spacewalks)
326.5000 to 328.5000		Radio astronomy (Jodrell Bank)
344.0000		Common airfield frequency
362.3000		Common airfield frequency
328.6000—335.4000		Aeronautical radionavigation — ILS glideslope beams paired with VORs in the 108—118 MHz band
335.4000—399.9000		Aeronautical mobile (military) using AM simplex, ground-to-air, air- to-air, tactical, etc.
360.0440 to 361.4400		Band has been used by US ATS-series satellites
399.9000—400.0500		Radionavigation by satellite. Doppler shift position fixing using US satellites (TRANSIT) and USSR (COSNAV) paired with 149.9—150.05 MHz band
400.0000—400.1500		Standard frequency and time signal satellites
401.0000—406.0000		Fixed and mobile, meteorological satellites, space-Earth communications
401.0000 to 402.0000		Space-Earth communications
401.0000 to 403.0000		Meteorological sondes & satellites
401.0000 to 405.0000		Military telemetry links
406.0000—406.1000		Mobile satellite space-Earth communications
406.05000		Emergency locator beacons (identification and location by satellite)
406.1000—410.0000		Fixed and mobile (government), radio astronomy & radio positioning aids
406.5000 to 409.0000		North Sea oil rig positioning aids
410.0000—415.0000		TETRA PMR, shared with government services
415.0000—420.0000		Government fixed, mobile and space research
412.0500		Frequency has been used by US ATS-series satellites
420.0000—450.0000		Fixed, mobile, amateur & radiolocation
420.0000 to 422.0000		Military MOULD links
422.0000 to 425.0000		Military & radio altimeters
425.0250 to 425.4750	445.5250 to 445.9750	PMR mobiles
425.5250 to 428.9750	440.0250 to 443.4750	PMR bases
429.0000 to 431.0000		Military & radiolocation
431.00625 to 431.99375	448.00625 to 448.99375	PMR mobiles (London only)
430.0000 to 440.0000		70cm amateur band & military (Syledis radiolocation system and MOULD links). SSB, NFM, CW, slow and fast scan TV, RTTY, Amtor, Packet, etc.
440.0250 to 443.4650	425.5250 to 428.9750	PMR bases. Many transport system users (taxis, buses etc.)
443.5000 to 445.5000		Military & radiolocation
445.5250 to 445.9750	425.0250 to 425.4750	PMR bases

From-to	Pairing	Allocation
446.0250–446.4750		PMR simplex 12.5 kHz spacing
446.00625–446.09375		PMR446 public simplex radio, 8 channels 12.5kHz spacing with 6.25 kHz offset using 500m watt hand-portables
446.4750	452.250	Fire channel 02 F
448.00625 to 448.99375	431.00625 to 431.99375	PMR bases (London area only)
449.7500 to 450.0000		Earth-space telecommand
450.0000–470.0000		Fixed & mobile (including marine). Mostly PMR with some emergency services, paging, telemetry, etc.
450.0000 to 453.0000	464.0000 to 467.0000	Extensively used for police bases and fixed links
451.4000		Fire brigade on-site handhelds Ch1F
451.4500		Fire brigade on-site handhelds Ch 2F
453.0250 to 453.9750	459.5250 to 460.4750	PMR Bases
454.0125 to 454.8375		Wide area paging systems
455.0000		BBC, ITV, ILR base units for OBs (some units paired with mobiles at to + 5.5 MHz). Airport ground services including tower relays (typically 455.5000, 455.4750, 455.9750 etc.)
455.5000 to 456.0000		Some PMR (Scotland) & airport ground services
456.0000 to 456.9750	461.50000 to 462.4750	PMR bases (extensively used at airports)
456.9250	462.4250	Short-term hire bases
457.0000 to 457.5000	462.5000 to 463.0000	Point-to-point links (fixed)
457.50625 to 458.49375	463.00625 to 463.99375	Scanning telemetry
457.5250	467.5250	On-board-ship communications (international)
457.5500	467.5500	On-board-ship communications (international)
457.5750	467.5750	On-board-ship communications (international)
457.5250	467.7500	On-board-ship communications (US/Canada system)
457.5500	467.7750	On-board-ship communications (US/Canada system)
457.5750	467.8000	On-board-ship communications (US/Canada system)
457.6000	467.8250	On-board-ship communications (US/Canada system)
458.5000 to 459.5000		Model control, paging, telemetry & local communications
458.5000 to 458.8000		Low-power (½ watt) telemetry
459.1000 to 459.5000	161.0000 to 161.0000	On-site paging systems (VHF channels are return 'acknowledge' signal)
459.5250 to 460.4750	453.0250 to 453.9750	PMR mobiles
460.5000 to 461.5000	467.0000 to 468.0000	Point-to-point links & some airport ground services, broadcast engineering, etc
461.2625		UK short-range business radio
461.4750		UK short-range business radio
461.4875		UK short-range business radio
461.5000 to 462.4750	456.0000 to 456.9750	PMR mobiles
462.4250	456.9250	Short-term hire channel mobiles
462.4251	462.4750	Long-term hire (single frequency simplex)
462.5000 to 463.0000	457.5000 to 458.5000	Point-to-point links (fixed)
463.0000 to 464.0000	457.5000 to 458.5000	Telemetry links (fixed)
464.0000		Spot frequency has been used by some US & French satellites
464.0000 to 467.0000	450.0000 to 453.0000	Emergency service mobiles and fixed links
466.0000		Spot frequency has been used by some Soviet ocean reconnaisance satellites

From-to	Pairing	Allocation
466.0625–466.0875		Wide area paging
467.0000 to 467.8250		Point-to-point links & ILR broadcast links using simplex & on-board-ship communications
467.5250	457.5250	On-board-ship communications (international)
467.5500	457.5500	On-board-ship communications (international)
467.5750	457.5750	On-board-ship communications (international)
467.7500	457.5250	On-board-ship communications (US/Canada system)
467.7750	457.5500	On-board-ship communications (US/Canada system)
467.8000	457.5750	On-board-ship communications (US/Canada system)
467.8250	457.6000	On-board-ship communications (US/Canada system)
467.8250 to 468.0000	455.0000 to 462.0000	Point-to-point links
468.5000 to 469.0000		Some outside broadcast links, model control and reserved for future PMR expansion
469.0000 to 470.0000		Some outside broadcast link talkback and mobiles
470.0000–854.0000		UK Band IV television broadcasting, studio talkback systems, radio astronomy & aeronautical radionavigation, Russian/CIS communication satellites
471.0000 to 585.0000		Television broadcasting Band IV
537.0000 to 544.0000	716.000 to 725.000	Studio talkback mobiles on unused broadcast channels
582.0000 to 590.0000		Aeronavigation ground radar (due to be phased out)
590.0000 to 598.0000		Aeronavigation ground radar
598.0000 to 606.0000		Aeronavigation ground radar (due to be phased out)
614.0000		Radio astronomy (Cambridge & Jodrell Bank)
610.0000 to 890.0000		Television broadcasting Band V
702.0000 to 726.0000		Soviet direct TV broadcast satellites
716.0000 to 725.0000	537.0000 to 544.0000	Studio talkback bases on unused broadcast channels
800.000–1000.000		Molniya communications satellites (data and NFM)
862.000–870.000		Fixed and mobile (not aeronautical)
862.000–863.000		UK emergency services
863.000–865.000		Cordless headphones
864.1000 to 868.1000		CT2 digital portable telephones
870.0000–889.0000		Fixed & mobile(mostly military), industrial, scientific & medical & anti-theft devices. ETACS (cellular telephone) in London area
872.0000 to 888.0000	917.0000 to 933.0000	ETACS (cellular telephones) 25 kHz steps with 12.5 kHz offset
886.0000 to 890.0000		Industrial, scientific & medical
888.0000 to 889.0000		Anti-theft devices (½ watt maximum)
890.0000–915.0000		GSM cellphones phone mobile Tx
915.0000–935.0000		Fixed & mobile (government) & space communications, residual analogue E-TACS cellular telephones
922.75000		Mir/Salyut TV picture downlinks
926.06000		Mir/Salyut voice & telecommand (NFM)
928.40000		Venera deep-space planetary probe
933.00000 to 935.00000		New UK personal radio system
935.0000–960.0000		GSM cellphones phone base Tx
960.0000–1215.0000		Aeronavigation (distance measuring equipment – DME) & TACANS (radar transponders – IFF)
1215.0000–1240.0000		Radiolocation and radionavigation by satellite
1240.0000–1296.0000		Radiolocation

From-to	Pairing	Allocation
1296.0000–1300.0000		Amateur radio 23cm band (NFM, SSB, WBTV etc.)
1300.0000–1365.0000		Amateur radio 23cm band & radiolocation (government)
1365.0000–1427.0000		Radiolocation, space research & satellite exploration
1400.0000 to 1427.0000		Earth exploration satellites, astronomy & space research
1427.0000–1429.0000		Fixed & mobile (government) & Earth-space satellite links
1429.0000–1450.0000		Fixed & mobile (government)
1450.0000–1525.0000		Fixed & mobile (telephony, telecontrol & telemetry)
1525.0000–1530.0000		Fixed & land mobile & satellites (space-Earth)
1530.0000–1544.0000		Land mobile & maritime mobile satellite services (space-Earth)
1544.0000–1545.0000		Mobile satellite services
1544.0000 to 1545.0000	1645.0000 to 1646.0000	Space-Earth distress service
1544.5000		NOAA9/10 search & rescue beacon locator downlink
1545.0000–1559.9000		Aeronautical mobile satellite service
1559.0000–1626.5000		Aeronautical radionavigation & navigation satellites & radio astronomy
1626.5000–1645.0000		Maritime mobile satellite service
1645.0000–1646.5000		Mobile satellite service
1645.0000 to 1646.0000	1544.0000 to 1545.0000	Earth-space distress
1646.5000–1660.0000		Aeronautical mobile, satellite services (uplinks) & astronomy
1660.0000–1668.0000		Fixed & mobile & astronomy
1668.0000–1670.0000		Fixed links (government) & astronomy
1670.0000–1700.0000		Fixed (PTO & government) & land mobile & meteorological satellites. Goes, NOAA and Meteosat transmissions — for details see satellite section
1700.0000–2000.0000		Fixed & land mobile (PTO & government), satellite operations & astronomy
1730.000–1780.000		PCN telephones portable unit Tx
1825.000–1875.000		PCN telephones base unit Tx

GLOSSARY OF ABBREVIATIONS AND DEFINITIONS USED IN TABLE 6.1

Aeronautical distress Frequencies allocated solely for use by aircraft in distress.

Aeronautical mobile Allocations for communication between aircraft and ground stations. The main international band lies between 118–137 MHz.

Aeronautical radionavigation Radio beacons for aircraft navigation. They include VHF omni-range (VOR), doppler VOR (DVOR), distance measuring equipment (DME), instrument landing systems (ILS), tactical navigation (TACAN), outer, middle and inner fan markers (OM, MM, IM), etc.

Aeronautical search and rescue Frequencies allocated solely for aircraft involved in search and rescue (SAR) duties.

Amateur The amateur service is for use by licensed individuals for the purpose of self-training and experimentation.

Astronomy Frequencies allocated for research into radio emissions from sources such as other galaxies.

Broadcast Transmissions intended for reception by a large group or even the general public.

BT British Telecom.

Carphone A communication system fitted to a vehicle which communicates with a base station connected to the public telephone system.

Citizens' Band A low-powered communications service available to the public.

Cordless phone A telephone handset that does not require direct connection to the exchange line.

COSPAS/SARSAT Joint US, USSR, Canadian and French rescue service using weather satellite to fix the position of emergency rescue beacons.

ELINT Electronic intelligence gathering (typically spy satellites).

Emergency service Allocations for police, fire and ambulance services.

EPIRB Emergency position indicating rescue beacon.

Fixed A base station linked to another base station or non-mobile facility such as a repeater. Often known as point-to-point services.

FSK Frequency shift keying.

IFF Identify – friend or foe.

ILR Independent local radio.

ISM Industrial, scientific and medical. These allocations are for equipment which use radio waves to function. These allocations are not for communication purposes.

Land mobile Communications between a fixed base and mobile or portable equipment or between the mobile stations themselves.

Locator The transmission of signals for navigation, position fixing and tracking.

Maritime mobile Services for ship-to-shore and ship-to-ship communications.

Message handling Similar to PMR but many stations operating through a central operator at a base station.

Meteorology The transmission of weather data from remote platforms such as sondes, buoys or satellites to ground stations.

Military British military allocations cover the Army, Royal Air Force, Royal Navy, Military Police and United States Air Force (USAF).

Mobile Any mobile service – air, marine or land.

Mobile satellite service Communication between a mobile station and satellite (usually the satellite is acting as a relay or repeater to a distant ground station).

MOD Ministry of Defence.

Model control The use of radio signals to control the movement of model boats, aircraft and cars.

MOULD British military communication system making extensive use of repeaters.

NOAA National Oceanic and Atmospheric Administration (USA).

On-site paging A paging service operating in a restricted area such as a hospital, factory or hotel.

Pager A miniature radio receiver which emits a tone when it receives a signal with its individually assigned code.

Positioning aid A beacon used to emit a transmission for precise positioning or navigation. Often used for positioning such things as oil rigs.

PMR Private mobile radio. Allocations for non-government users for communication between base stations and mobile units.

PMR446 Pan-European public radio system allocation in the 446 MHz range using 500m milliwatt handhelds with 500m milliwatt maximum radiated power.

Radio altimeter The use of radio signals to measure the height of an aircraft above ground.

Radio microphone A microphone used in broadcast studios, theatres and the film industry where the unit transmits the sound as a low-powered radio signal which is picked up by a remote receiver and then amplified.

Radiophone See **Carphone**.

SARBE Search and rescue beacon. A small radio beacon attached to a lifejacket or dinghy.

Satellite navigation Position fixing by reference to transmissions from a satellite.

Selcal Selective calling system where a receiver only activates when it receives a pre-determined code.

Slick marker A low-powered floating beacon used to check the movement of oil slicks.

SRBR UK Short Range Business Radio system operating on three channels in the 461 MHz range, due to be phased out in 2003.

Standard frequency Transmission from a highly stable transmitter which is accurate enough to be used for calibration and reference. The signals often include coded signals of highly accurate time as well.

TACS Total access communications system (cellular telephones).

Telecontrol A signal containing command information to control remote equipment.

Telemetry A radio signal containing data in coded form.

Television A radio signal containing visual images.

TETRA TErrestrial Trunked Radio, a digital radio system used for emergency services across Europe and for civil trunked PMR

Weather satellite A space satellite that sends weather pictures back to an earth station.

Wide area paging A paging service not confined to a private site.

AERONAUTICAL BANDS

Aeronautical and marine bands, unlike all other bands, are standard worldwide. Aircraft transmissions are of two kinds: civilian and military. Civilian aircraft transmissions use two bands – HF using SSB for long-distance communication, and VHF for communications up to distances of several hundred miles. All communications (civilian and military) are amplitude modulated.

A list of civilian and military airports and corresponding transmission frequencies are given and are believed to be current. However, it should be noted that they are occasionally changed.

Table 6.2 British and Irish airports and air/ground stations

Airfield				
Aberdeen (Dyce)			TOWER	118.100
EGPD	civ 7 miles NW of Aberdeen		GROUND	121.700
MET	125.725 (Scottish Volmet)118.300 (Kirkwall Met)		VDF	120.400, 121.250, 128.300
ATIS	121.850, 114.300		RADAR	120.400, 128.300
APPROACH	120.400		FIRE VEHICLES	121.600

Airfield

Aberporth
EGUC	mil 5 miles NE of Cardigan
AFIS	122.150, 259.000

Abingdon
EGUD	mil 5 miles SW of Oxford
TOWER	130.250, 256.500
SRE	122.100, 123.300, 120.900, 256.500

Alconbury
EGWZ	mil 4 miles NW of Huntingdon
ATIS	231.175
MATZ	see Wyton
TOWER	122.100, 383.45, 257.800, 315.100
GROUND	259.825
DISPATCH	342.225
DEPARTURE	134.050, 375.535
COMMAND POST	278.050, 340.125
METRO	358.600, 284.925

Alderney
EGJA	civ Channel Islands
TOWER	125.350
APPROACH	128.650 (Guernsey)

Andrewsfield
EGSL	civ near Braintree (Essex)
A/G	130.550

Audley End
EG	civ near Saffron Walden (Essex)
A/G	122.350

Badminton
EG	civ 6 miles NE of Chipping Sodbury
A/G	123.175

Bagby civ Thirsk
A/G	123.250

Baldonnel/Casement
EIME	civ Republic of Ireland
APPROACH	122.000
TOWER	123.500
GROUND	123.100
RADAR	122.800 122.300 (Dublin Military)
PAR	129.700

Bantry
EI	civ Republic of Ireland
A/G	122.400

Airfield

Barra
EGPR	civ Traigh Mhor (Western Isles)
AFIS	130.650

Barrow
EGNL	civ North end of Walney Island
A/G	123.200
TOWER	123.200

Barton
EG	5 miles W of Manchester
A/G	122.700

Battersea Heliport
EGLW	civ River Thames at Battersea
TOWER	122.900

Beccles Heliport
EGSM	civ 2 miles SE of Beccles (Suffolk)
A/G	134.600

Bedford
EGVW	mil 5 miles N of city at Thurleigh
MATZ	124.400
APPROACH	130.700, 124.400, 265.300, 277.250
TOWER	130.000, 337.925
VDF	130.700, 130.000, 124.400, 277.250
PAR	118.375, 356.700

Belfast Aldergrove
EGAA	civ 13 miles NW of Belfast
APPROACH	120.000, 310.000
TOWER	118.300, 310.000
DISPATCHER	241.825
GROUND	121.750
VDF	120.900
RADAR	120.000, 120.900, 310.000
FIRE VEHICLES	121.600

Belfast City
EGAC	civ 2 miles E of city centre
APPROACH	130.850
TOWER	130.750
SRE	134.800

Bembridge
EGHJ	civ Isle of Wight
A/G	123.250

Benbecula
EGPL	civ
APPROACH	119.200
TOWER	119.200

Airfield

Benson

EGUB	mil 10 miles SE Oxford city
MATZ	120.900
APPROACH	120.900, 122.1, 362.3, 358.800
TOWER	122.100, 279.350
GROUND	340.325
VDF	119.000
SRE	119.000

Bentwaters

EGVJ	mil 6 miles NE Woodbridge (Suffolk)
ATIS	341.650
MATZ	119.000
APPROACH	119.000, 362.075
TOWER	122.100, 264.925, 257.800
GROUND	244.775
DISPATCH	356.825
DEPARTURE	258.975
SRE/PAR	119.000, 362.075
COMMAND POST	386.900
due for closure	

Biggin Hill

EGKB	civ 4 miles N Westerham (Kent)
ATIS	121.875
APPROACH	129.400
TOWER	138.400
RADAR	132.700 (Thames)

Birmingham

EGBB	civ 6 miles SE of city at Elmdon
ATIS	120.725
ATC	131.325
APPROACH	131.325
TOWER	118.300
GROUND	121.800
VDF	131.325
RADAR	131.325, 118.050
FIRE VEHICLES	121.600

Blackbushe

EGLK	civ 4 miles W Camberley (Hants)
AFIS	122.300

Blackpool

EGNH	civ South of Town at Squire's Gate
APPROACH	135.950
TOWER	118.400
VDF	135.950, 118.400
SRE	119.950

Airfield

Bodmin

EG	civ 2 miles NE Bodmin (Cornwall)
A/G	122.700

Booker see Wymcombe

Boscombe Down

EGDM	mil 5 miles N Salisbury
MATZ	126.700, 380.025
ATIS	263.500
APPROACH	126.700, 276.850, 291.650
TOWER	130.000, 370.100
PAR	130.750
SRE	126.700

Boulmer

EGOM	SAR 8 miles E of Alnwick
A/G	Boulmer Rescue 123.100, 254.425, 282.800, 299.100

Bourn

EGSN	civ 7 miles W Cambridge
A/G	129.800

Bournemouth

EGHH	civ 4 miles NE Bournemouth
ATIS	121.950
APPROACH	119.625
TOWER	125.600
GROUND	121.700
RADAR	119.625, 118.650
FIRE VEHICLES	121.600

Bridlington

EG	civ
A/G	123.250

Bristol

EGGD	civ 7 miles SW Bristol
ATIS	121.750
APPROACH	132.400
TOWER	133.850
VDF	132.400
SRE	124.350

Brize Norton

EGVN	mil 5 miles SW Witney (Oxon)
MATZ	119.000
ATIS	235.150
APPROACH	133.750, 119.000, 342.450, 362.300
TOWER	126.500, 257.800, 381.200
GROUND	126.500, 370.300
DIRECTOR	130.075, 382.550
RADAR	134.300, 257.100

Airfield		
Brough	EG	civ 6 miles W of Hull
APPROACH		118.225
TOWER		130.550
Caernarfon		
	EG	civ
	A/G	122.250
Cambridge		
	EGSC	civ 2 miles E of city
AP/DF		123.600
TOWER		122.200, 372.450
SRE		130.750
FIRE		121.600 fire vehicles
Cardiff (Rhoose)		
	EGFF	civ 12 miles SW of Cardiff
MET		128.600 London Volmet South
ATIS		119.475
AP/DF		125.850, 277.225
TOWER		125.000
RAD/PAR		125.850, 120.050
Carlisle (Crosby)		
	EGNC	civ 5 miles NE of Carlisle
APPROACH/ TOWER		123.600
DF		123.600
Carrickfin	EI	civ Republic of Ireland
	A/G	129.800
Chichester		
	EGHR	civ N of Chichester (Sussex)
APPROACH		122.500
TOWER		120.650
A/G		122.450
VDF		122.450
Chivenor		
	EGDC	mil 4 miles W of Barnstaple (Devon)
MATZ/APP		130.200, 122.100, 362.300, 364.775
TOWER/GROUND		122.100, 362.450
GROUND		122.100, 379.925
VDF		130.200
PAR		123.300
SRE		122.100, 362.300

Airfield		
Church Fenton		
	EGXG	mil 6 miles NW of Selby (Yorks)
MATZ/APPROACH		126.500, 282.075, 362.300
TOWER		122.100, 262.700, 257.800
GROUND		122.100, 340.200
PAR		123.300
SRE		231.00, 362.300
DEPARTURE (Linton)		129.150, 381.075, 292.800
Clacton	EG	civ West of Clacton (Essex)
	A/G	122.325
Colerne	EG	mil near Bath
	A/G	122.100
Coltishall		
	EGYC	mil 9 miles N of Norwich (Norfolk)
MATZ/APPROACH		125.900, 122.100, 379.275, 293.425, 342.250
TOWER		122.100, 142.290, 288.850
GROUND		269.450
VDF		125.900, 122.100, 293.425, 342.250
SRE		125.900, 123.300, 293.425, 342.250
PAR		123.300
DIRECTOR		244.750
Compton Abbas		
	EGHA	civ 2 miles E of Shaftesbury (Dorset)
	A/G	122.700
Coningsby		
	EGXC	mil 15 miles NE of Sleaford (Lincs)
MATZ		120.800
APPROACH		120.800, 122.100, 312.225, 362.300
TOWER		121.100, 120.800, 275.875
GROUND		122.100, 318.150
SRE		120.800
PAR		123.300, 312.225, 362.300
DEPARTURE		344.625
Connaught		
	EIKN	civ Republic of Ireland
TOWER		130.700
GROUND		121.900
Cork	EICK	civ Republic of Ireland
MET		127.000 Dublin Volmet
APPROACH		119.900
TOWER		119.300, 121.700
GROUND		121.800

Airfield		
Cosford EGWC	civ 9 miles NW of Wolverhampton	
APPROACH	276.125, 362.300	
TOWER	122.100, 357.125	
Cottesmore		
EGXJ	mil 4 miles NE of Oakham (Leics)	
MATZ	123.300	
APPROACH/DF	123.300, 380.950	
TOWER	122.100, 130.200, 370.050, 257.800	
GROUND	122.200, 336.375	
PAR	123.300	
SRE	123.300, 380.950	
DEPARTURE	130.200, 376.575	
Coventry		
EGBE	civ 3 miles S of Coventry	
APPROACH	119.250	
TOWER	119.250, 124.800	
GROUND	121.700	
VDF	119.250, 122.000	
SRE	119.250, 122.000	
FIRE	121.600 fire vehicles	
Cranfield		
EGTC	civ 4 miles E of M1 junctions 13/14	
ATIS	121.875	
APPROACH	122.850, 362.150	
TOWER	123.200, 122.850, 341.800	
VDF	122.850, 123.200, 124.550	
RAD	122.850, 372.100	
Cranwell		
EGYD	mil 4 miles NW of Sleaford (Lincs)	
MATZ	119.000	
APPROACH	122.100, 119.000, 340.475, 362.300	
TOWER	122.100, 379.525, 257.800	
GROUND	297.900	
SRE	123.300	
PAR	123.300	
Crossland Moor		
EG	civ 3 miles SW Huddersfield	
A/G	122.200	
Croughton		
EG	mil	
A/G	343.600, 344.850	
Crowfield EG	civ	
A/G	122.775	

Airfield		
Culdrose		
EGDR	mil 1 mile SE of Helston (Cornwall)	
ATIS	305.600	
APPROACH/MATZ	134.050, 241.950	
TOWER	122.100, 123.300, 380.225	
GROUND	310.200	
RADAR	122.100, 134.050, 241.950, 339.950	
PAR	122.100, 123.300, 259.750, 339.950	
Cumbernauld		
EGPG	civ 6 miles SW of Falkirk (Strathclyde)	
Denham		
EGLD	civ 1 mile N of M1 junction 1 (Bucks)	
A/G	130.725	
Dishforth		
EGXD	mil 4 miles E of Ripon (Yorks)	
MATZ	Leeming	
APPROACH	122.100, 379.675, 362.300	
TOWER	122.100, 259.825	
Dounreay Thurso		
EGPY	civ 8 miles W of Thurso	
AFIS	122.400 (only by prior arrangement)	
Dublin EIDW	civ	
MET	122.700	
ATIS	118.250	
APPROACH	121.100	
TOWER	118.600	
GROUND	121.800	
SRE	119.550, 118.500, 118.600, 121.100	
Dundee		
EGPN	civ 2 Miles W of Dundee	
APPROACH/TOWER	122.900	
Dunkeswell		
EG	civ 5 miles NW of Honiton (Devon)	
A/G	123.475	
Dunsfold		
EGTD	civ 9 miles S of Guildford (Surrey)	
APPROACH	122.550, 312.625, 367.375	
TOWER	124.325, 375.400	
VDF	122.550, 124.325	
RAD	119.825, 122.550, 291.900	
Duxford EG	civ 9 miles S of Cambridge	
AFIS	122.075	

Airfield		
Earls Colne		
	EGSR	civ 5 miles SE of Halstead (Essex)
	A/G	122.425
East Midlands		
	EGNX	civ Castle Donnington, off M1
	MET	126.600 (London Volmet North)
	APPROACH	119.650
	TOWER	124.000
	GROUND	121.900
	VDF	119.650
	SRE	124.000, 120.125
	FIRE	121.600 (fire vehicles)
Edinburgh		
	EGPH	civ 8 miles W of Edinburgh
	MET	125.725 Scottish Volmet
	ATIS	132.075
	APPROACH	121.200, 130.400 (departing gliders, 257.800
	TOWER	118.700, 257.800
	GROUND	121.750, 257.800
	VDF	121.200, 118.700
	RAD	121.200, 128.975
	FIRE	121.600 (fire vehicles)
Elstree	EGTR	civ 12 miles NW London city centre
	A/G	122.400
Elvington		
	EGYK	mil
See Church Fenton		
Enniskillen St Angelo		
	EGAB	civ 5 miles N Enniskillen (N. Ireland)
	A/G	123.200
Enstone	EG	civ 5 miles SE of Chipping Norton
	A/G	129.875
Exeter	EGTE	civ 4 miles E of Exeter
APPROACH/DF		128.150
TOWER		119.800
SRE		128.150, 119.050
Fairford	EGVA	mil N of Swindon
MATZ/APPROACH		Brize Norton
TOWER		119.150, 357.575
GROUND		259.975
DISPATCHER		379.475
COMMAND POST		371.200, 307.800
METRO		358.600

Airfield		
Fairoaks		
	EGTF	civ 3 miles N of Woking
AFIS and A/G		123.425
Farnborough		
	EGUF	mil W of A325
	EGLF	civ
	A/G	130.050
	APPROACH	134.350, 336.275
	TOWER	122.500, 357.400
	PAR	130.050, 353.850
	DISPATCHER	254.850
Fenland	EGCL	civ Holbeach (Lincolnshire)
AFIS and A/G		122.925
Fife see Glenrothes		
Filton (Bristol)		
	EGTG	mil 4 miles N of Bristol
	APPROACH	122.275, 127.975, 256.125
	TOWER	124.950, 342.025
	VDF	122.275
	SRE	132.350
Finningly		
	EGXI	mil SE of Doncaster
	MATZ	120.350
	APPROACH	120.350, 358.775
	TOWER	122.100, 379.550
	GROUND	340.175
	SRE	120.350, 285.125, 315.500, 344.000
	PAR	123.300, 383.500, 385.400
Flotta	EG	civ Centre of Orkney Island
	A/G	122.150
Galway (Carnmore)		
	EICM	civ Republic of Ireland
A/G/TOWER		122.500
Gamston (Retford)		
	EGNE	civ
	A/G	130.475
Gatwick see London Gatwick		

(Photographs by Ian Doyle)

Airfield		
Glasgow		
	EGPF	Civ 6 miles W of City Centre
	MET	125.725 (Scottish Voomet), 135.375 (London Volmet Main)
	ATIS	115.400
	APPROACH	119.100
	TOWER	118.800
	GROUND	121.700
	RADAR	119.100, 119.300, 121.300
	FIRE VEHICLES	121.600
Glenrothes (Fife)		
	EGPJ	civ
	A/G	130.450
Goodwood see Chichester		
Gloucester (Staverton)		
	EGBJ	civ Gloucester and Cheltenham
	APPROACH	125.650, 120.970
	TOWER	125.650
	VDF	125.650, 122.900
	SRE	122.900
	FIRE VEHICLES	121.600
Great Yarmouth		
	EGSD	gov North Denes
	A/G	120.450, 122.375
	HF A/G	3.488, 5.484 MHz
Guernsey		
	EGJB	civ 3 miles S of St Peter Port
	ATIS	109.400
	APPROACH	128.650
	TOWER	119.950
	GROUND	121.800
	VDF	128.650, 124.500
	SRE	118.900, 124.500
Halfpenny Green		
	EGBO	civ 6 miles W of Dudley
	AFIS	123.000
	GROUND	121.950
Hatfield		
	EGTH	civ 2 miles S Welwyn Garden City
	APPROACH	123.350, 343.700
	TOWER	130.800, 359.450
	SRE	123.350, 119.300, 343.700

Airfield		
Haverfordwest		
	EGFE	mil 2 miles N of town
	AFIS	122.200
Hawarden		
	EGNR	civ 4 miles W of Chester
	APPROACH	123.350
	TOWER	124.950, 336.325
	VDF	123.350, 129.850
	RADAR	129.850
Heathrow see London Heathrow		
Henstridge		
	EGHS	civ Somerset S of A30
	A/G	130.275
Hethel EGSK	civ 7 miles SW of Norwich	
	A/G	122.350
Honington		
	EHXH	mil N of Bury St Edmunds (Suffolk)
	MATZ	129.050
	APPROACH	129.050, 309.950, 344.000
	TOWER	122.100, 283.275, 257.900
	GROUND	241.975
	DEPARTURE	123.300, 309.950
	SRE	129.050, 254.875, 309.950, 338.975, 344.000
	PAR	123.300, 358.750, 385.400
Hucknall		
	EGNA	civ 1 miles SW of town (Notts)
	A/G	130.800
Humberside		
	EGNJ	civ 15 miles E of Scunthorpe
	APPROACH	123.150
	TOWER	118.550
	VDF	123.150
	FIRE VEHICLES	121.600
Inverness (Dalcross)		
	EGPE	civ 8 miles NE Inverness
	MET	125.725 (Scottish Volmet)
	APPROACH/TOWER	122.600
Ipswich EGSE	civ 2 miles SE Ipswitch	
	A/G	118.325
Islay (Port Ellen)		
	EGPI	civ South end of Island
	AFIS	123.150

Airfield

Jersey EGJJ civ 3 miles W of St. Helier
MET 128.600 (London Volmet South)
ATIS 112.200
APPROACH 120.300
TOWER 199.450
GROUND 121.900
FIRE VEHICLES 121.600

Kemble EGDK mil 4 miles SW Cirencester
MATZ 118.900
APPROACH 118.900, 123.300
TOWER 118.900

Kinloss EGQK mil (3 miles NE of Foress (Grampian)
MET 118.300
MATZ Lossiemouth
APPROACH 119.350, 362.300, 376.650
TOWER 122.100, 336.350, 257.800
DISPATCHER 358.475
OPERATIONS 259.825
SRE 123.300, 259.975, 311.325
PAR 123.300, 370.050, 376.525

Kirkwall EGPA civ (Orkney
MET 118.300
APPROACH/TOWER 118.300

Lakenheath
EGUL mil (5 miles N of Barton Mills (Suffolk)
APPROACH 123.300, 398.350
RAPCON 398.350
TOWER 122.100, 358.675, 257.800
GROUND 397.975
DISPATCHER 300.825
DEPARTURE 123.300, 315.575
COMMAND POST 269.075
METRO 257.750
SRE/PAR 123.300, 243.600, 262.925, 290.825, 338.675
SRE/PAR 149.650 (NFM)

Land's End (St. Just)
EGHC civ 6 miles W of Penzance
A/G 130.700
APPROACH/TOWER 130.700

Lasham EGHL civ 5 miles S of Basingstoke
A/G 122.875

Lashenden
EGHK civ 10 miles SE of Maidstone
A/G 122.000

Airfield

Leavesden
EGTI civ 2 miles NW of Watford
APPROACH/TOWER 122.150
VDF 122.150
SRE 122.400

Leconfield Rescue
EGXV mil
A/G 122.100, 244.875, 282.800

Leeds-Bradford
EGNM civ Half way between Leeds Bradford
MET 126.600 (London Volmet North)
APPROACH/VDF 123.750
TOWER 120.300
SRE 121.050
FIRE VEHICLES 121.600

Leeming
EGXE mil Northallerton (Yorks)
APPROACH 127.750, 387.800
TOWER 122.100, 382.100, 394.500
VDF 132.400, 122.100, 359.200, 362.300, 387.800
PAR 122.100, 248.000, 352.900
SRE 127.750, 339.400

Lee-on-Solent
EGUS mil 4 miles west of Gosport
TOWER 135.700, 315.650

Leicester
EGBG civ 4 miles S of Leicester
A/G/FIS 122.250

Lerwick Tingwall
EG civ Shetland Isles
A/G 122.600

Leuchars
EGQL mil 7 miles SE of Dundee
MATZ/LARS 126.500
APPROACH 126.500, 255.400, 362.300
TOWER 122.100, 258.925
GROUND 120.800, 259.850
DISPATCHER 285.025
VDF 126.500
SRE 123.300, 292.475
PAR 123.300, 268.775, 370.075

Airfield		
Linton-on-Ouse		
EGXU	mil 10 miles NW of York	
MATZ/LARS	129.150, 121.100, 292.800, 344.000	
APPROACH	129.150, 292.800, 362.675, 362.300	
TOWER	122.100, 257.800, 300.425	
GROUND	122.100, 340.025	
DEPARTURE	129.150, 381.075, 292.800	
SRE	129.150, 122.100, 344.000, 344.475	
PAR	123.300, 129.150, 259.875, 358.525	
Liverpool		
EGGP	civ 6 miles SE of city	
MET	126.600 (London Volmet North)	
APPROACH	119.850	
TOWER	118.100	
RADAR	18.450, 119.850	
Llanbedr		
EGOD	mil 3 miles S of Harlech	
APPROACH	122.500, 386.675	
TOWER	122.500, 380.175	
RADAR/PAR/VDF	122.500, 370.300, 386.675	
London City		
EGLC	civ London Dockland	
TOWER	119.425, 118.075	
RADAR	132.700 (Thames), 128.025 (City)	
FIRE VEHICLES	121.600	
London Gatwick		
EGKK	civ 28 miles S of London	
MET	135.375 (London Volmet Main)	
ATIS	128.475	
APPROACH	125.875, 134.225	
TOWER	124.225, 134.225	
CLEARANCE	121.950	
GROUND	121.800	
RADAR	134.225, 118.600, 119.600, 129.275	
FIRE VEHICLES	121.600	
London Heathrow		
EGLL	civ 14 miles W of London	
MET	135.375 (London Volmet Main)	
ATIS	115.100 (Biggin , 113.750 (Bovingdon)	
ATIS	133.075	
APPROACH	119.200, 120.400, 119.500, 127.550	
TOWER	118.700, 124.475	
CLEARANCE	121.700	
GROUND	121.900	
RADAR	119.200, 119.500, 127.550, 120.400	
FIRE VEHICLES	121.600	

Airfield		
London Stansted		
EGSS	civ 30 miles N of London	
MET	135.375 (London Volmet Main)	
ATIS	127.175	
APPROACH	125.550	
TOWER	118.150	
GROUND	121.700	
VDF	125.550, 126.950, 118.150, 123.800	
RADAR	125.550, 126.950, 123.800	
FIRE VEHICLES	121.600	
Londonderry		
EGAE	civ Northern Ireland	
APPROACH	123.625	
TOWER	122.850	
FIRE	121.600	
Lossiemouth		
EGQS	mil 5 miles N of Elgin (Grampian)	
MATZ/LARS	119.350, 376.650	
APPROACH	119.350, 362.300, 398.100	
TOWER	118.900, 122.100, 337.750	
GROUND	299.400	
SRE	123.300, 259.975, 311.325	
PAR	123.300, 250.050, 312.400	
VDF	119.350,	
Luton	EGGW	civ SE of Luton
	MET	128.600 (London Volmet South)
	ATIS	120.575
	APPROACH	129.550, 128.750, 127.300, 259.875
	TOWER	119.975
	GROUND	121.750
	VDF	129.550, 127.300, 128.750
	SRE	128.750, 127.300
	FIRE VEHICLES	121.600
Lydd	EGMD	civ Off B2075 Lydd/New Romney Road
APPROACH/TOWER	120.700	
	SRE	131.300
Lyneham		
EGDL	mil 8 miles SW M4 junction 16 (Wilts)	
ATIS	381.000	
APPROACH	118.425, 123.400, 359.500, 362.300	
TOWER	118.425, 122.100, 386.825	
GROUND	118.425, 122.100, 340.175	
DISPATCHER	265.950	
OPERATIONS	254.650	
VDF	123.400	
PAR	123.300, 375.200, 385.400	
SRE	123.400, 300.475, 344.000	

Airfield		
Macrihanish		
	EGQJ	mil 4 miles W of Campbeltown
	MATZ	125.900, 122.100, 344.525, 362.300
	APPROACH	125.900, 122.100,3 44.525, 362.300
	TOWER	122.100, 358.600, 257.800
	PAR	123.300, 337.975, 385.400
	SRE	125.900, 123.300, 259.925, 344.000
Manchester		
	EGCC	civ 10 miles S of city centre
	MET	135.375, 126.600, 127.000 (Dublin Volmet)
	ATIS	128.175
	APPROACH	119.400, 121.350
	TOWER	118.625
	GROUND	121.700, 121.850
	RADAR	119.400, 121.350
	FIRE VEHICLES	121.600
Manchester (Barton)		
	EGCB	civ 6 miles W of Manchester
	A/G	122.700
Manston		
	EGUM	mil 4 miles NW of Ramsgate (Kent)
	EGMH	civ
	MATZ	126.350
	APPROACH	126.350, 122.100, 362.300, 379.025
	TOWER	128.775, 122.100, 344.350, 257.800
	VDF	126.350, 129.450
	PAR	123.300, 118.525, 312.350, 385.400
	SRE	126.350, 123.300, 338.625, 344.000
Marham		
	EGYM	mil Near Swaffham (Norfolk)
	MATZ	124.150
	APPROACH	124.150, 291.950, 362.300 (Eastern Radar)
	TOWER	122.100, 337.900, 257.800
	DISPATCHER	241.450
	OPERATIONS	312.550
	VDF	124.150, 122.100
	PAR	123.300, 379.650, 385.400
	SRE	124.150, 293.775, 344.000
Merryfield		
	EG	mil N of Ilminster (Somerset)
	APPROACH	127.350, 276.700, 362.300 (Yeovil)
	TOWER	122.100, 287.100

Airfield		
Middle Wallop		
	EGVP	mil 6 miles SW of Andover (Hants)
	MATZ	Boscombe Down
	APPROACH	126.700, 122.100, 312.000
	TOWER	122.100, 372.650
	PAR	364.825
	SRE	312.675
Mildenhall		
	EGUN	mil Near Barton Mills (Suffolk)
	ATIS	277.075
	APPROACH	128.900
	TOWER	122.550, 258.825
	GROUND	380.150
	COMMAND POST	379.850, 312.450
	MAINTENANCE	254.625
	METRO	257.750
	NAVY DUTY	142.850 (NFM)
	AIR MOBILITY COM	379.850 See also Honington for MATZ/ APP/DEPART
Mona	EG	mil 10 miles W of Menai Bridge
	AFIS	122.000
	APPROACH	379.700
	TOWER	358.750
See also Valley		
Netheravon		
	EGDN	mil Near Armesbury (Wilts)
	A/G/TOWER	128.300, 253.500
	APPROACH	362.225
	TOWER	290.950
Netherthorpe		
	EGNF	civ 3 miles NW of Worksop
	AFIS	123.275
	A/G	123.275
Newcastle		
	EGNT	civ 5 miles NW of Newcastle
	MET	126.600 (London Volmet North)
	ATIS	114.250
	APPROACH	124.375, 284.600
	TOWER	119.700
	VDF	118.500, 119.700, 126.350
	RADAR	126.350, 118.500
	FIRE	121.600
Newquay See St Mawgan		

Airfield		
Newton	EGXN	mil 6 miles E of Nottingham
	APPROACH	122.100, 251.725, 362.300
	TOWER	122.100, 257.800, 375.425
Newtownards		
	EGAD	civ 2 miles SE of town centre
	A/G	123.500
North Denes	See Great Yarmouth	
North Weald		
	EGSX	mil NE of Epping (Essex)
	A/G	123.525
Northampton		
	EGBK	civ 5 miles NE of city
	AFIS/A/G	122.700
Northolt		
	EGWU	mil Close to Uxbridge (London area)
	ATIS	300.350
	APPROACH/VDF	126.450, 344.975, 362.300
	TOWER	126.450, 257.800, 312.350
	OPERATIONS	244.425
	SRE	375.500, 379.425
	PAR	130.350, 385.400
Norwich	EGSH	civ 3 miles N of Norwich
	MET	128.600 (London Volmet South)
	APPROACH	119.350
	TOWER	124.250
	SRE	119.350, 118.475
	FIRE	121.600
Nottingham		
	EGBN	civ Near Tollerton
	A/G	122.800
Odiham	EGVO	mil 8 miles N of Alton (Hants)
	ATIS	276.175
	MATZ	Farnborough
	APPROACH	122.100, 125.250, 315.975, 362.300
	TOWER	122.100, 309.625, 257.800
	PAR	123.300, 385.400
	SRE	386.775
Old Sarum		
	EG	civ 2 miles N of Salisbury (Wilts)
	A/G	123.575
Old Warden		
	EG	civ 2 miles W of Biggleswade (Beds)
	A/G	123.050

Airfield		
Oxford (Kidlington)		
	EGTK	civ 6 miles NW of Oxford
	ATIS	121.950
	AFIS	119.800
	A/G	118.875
	APPROACH	125.325
	TOWER	118.875
	GROUND	121.750
	VDF	125.325
Panshangar		
	EG	civ 4 miles W of Hertford
	AFIS	120.250
Penzance Heliport		
	EGHK	civ 1 miles E of Penzance
	A/G	118.100
Perth (Scone)		
	EGPT	civ 3 miles NE of Perth
	APPROACH/VDF	122.300
	TOWER	119.800
Peterborough (Con)		
	EGSF	civ 8 miles S of Peterborough
	A/G	129.725
Peterborough (Sib)		
	EGSP	civ
	A/G	122.300
Plymouth		
	EGHD	civ 4 miles N of Plymouth
	APPROACH	133.550
	TOWER	122.600
	VDF	133.550, 122.600
Pocklington		
	EG	civ
	A/G	130.100
Popham	EG	civ Near junction 8 of M3 (Hants)
	A/G	129.800
Portishead Radio		
	EG	civ B.T. message handling service
	A/G	131.625

Airfield

Portland

EGDP	mil 4 miles S of Weymouth
MATZ	124.150, 317.800
APPROACH	124.150, 122.100, 362.300
TOWER	122.100, 123.300, 124.150, 291.000, 362.300
SRE	124.150, 122.100, 317.800, 362.300
PAR	387.500, 362.300

Predannack

EG	civ Near Lizard Point (Cornwall)
TOWER	338.975, 370.000 See also Culdrose

Prestwick

EGPK	civ 28 miles S of Glasgow
MET	125.725 (Scottish Volmet)
ATIS	127.125
APPROACH	120.550, 386.925
TOWER	118.150, 121.800
RADAR	120.550, 119.450
FIRE	121.600
ROYAL NAVY	OPS 337.750

Redhill EGKR civ 1 mile E of town (Surrey)

AFIS/TOWER	120.275

Retford (Gamston)

EGNE	civ 3 miles S of Town (Notts)
A/G	130.475

Rochester

EGTO	civ 2 miles S of Town (Kent)
AFIS	122.250

St Athan

EGDX	mil 10 miles W of Barry (S Glamorgan)
APPROACH	122.100, 277.225, 357.175
TOWER	122.100, 257.800, 336.525
SRE	123.300, 340.100, 344.000, 380.125, 385.400

St Mawgan

EGDG	mil 5 miles NE of Newquay
MATZ	126.500
APPROACH	126.500, 122.100, 125.550, 357.200, 362.300
TOWER	123.400, 122.100, 241.825
DISPATCHER	245.600
OPERATIONS	260.000
VDF	126.500, 125.550
PAR	123.300, 336.550, 385.400
SRE	125.550, 344.000, 360.550

Airfield

Salisbury Plain

EG	mil
A/G	122.750, 253.500

Sandown EG civ Isle of Wight

A/G	123.500

Scampton

EGXP	mil 5 miles N of Lincoln
APPROACH	312.500, 362.300
TOWER	122.100, 282.400, 257.800
GROUND	372.500
DEPARTURE	249.850, 362.300
VDF	252.525
RADAR	127.350, 357.050, 344.000

Scatsta EGPM civ

APPROACH	123.600
TOWER	123.600
SRE	122.400
FIRE	121.600

Scilly Isles

EGHE	civ St Mary's Island
APPROACH/TOWER	123.150

Seething EG civ SE of Norwich

A/G	122.600

Shannon

EINN	civ Republic of Ireland
MET	127.000 (Dublin Volmet)
ATIS	130.950
APPROACH	121.400, 120.200
OCEANIC DEPARTURE	121.700
TOWER	118.700
GROUND	121.800
RADAR	121.400

Shawbury

EGOS	mil 10 miles NE of Shrewsbury
MATZ	124.150, 254.200
APPROACH	124.150, 276.075, 362.300
TOWER	122.100, 269.100, 257.800
GROUND	337.900
SRE	124.150, 344.000
PAR	123.300, 356.975, 385.400

Sherburn-in-Elmet

EGCL	civ Sherburn (Yorkshire)
A/G	122.600

81

Airfield

Shipdham

	EG	civ 4 miles S East Derham (Norfolk)
AFIS/A/G	119.950	

Sheffield EG civ 3 miles NE of city

Shobdon

EGBS	civ 10 miles W of Leominster	
A/G	123.500	

Shoreham

EGKA	civ 1 mile W of town	
A/G	123.150	
ATIS	121.750	
APPROACH	123.150	
TOWER	125.400	
VDF	123.150	

Sibson see Peterborough

Silverstone

EG	civ Northamptonshire	
TOWER/A/G	121.075 9 (by arrangement only)	

Skegness EG civ 2 miles N of town
A/G 130.450

Sleap EG civ 10 miles N of Shrewsbury
A/G 122.450

Sligo EISG civ Republic of Ireland
AFIS/TOWER/A/G 122.100

Southampton

EGHI	civ 1 mile W of Eastleigh	
MET	128.600 (London Volmet South)	
ATIS	113.350	
ATC/APPROACH	120.225, 128.850, 131.000	
TOWER	118.200	
RADAR	120.225, 128.850	
FIRE	121.600	

Southend

EGMC	civ 2 miles N of town	
MET	128.600 (London Volmet South)	
ATIS	121.800	
APPROACH	128.950	
TOWER	127.725	
SRE	128.950	

Stanford EG mil 1 mile NW M20 junction 11 (Kent)
A/G OPERATIONS 307.800

Airfield

Stansted see London Stansted

Stapelford

EGSG	civ 5 miles N of Romford (Essex)	
A/G	122.800	

Stornoway

EGPO	civ 3 miles E of town (Hebrides)	
MET	125.750 (Scottish Volmet)	
AFIS/APPROACH	123.500	
TOWER	123.500	

Strathallan

EG	civ Tayside	
A/G	129.900	

Sturgate

EGCS	civ 6 miles SE of Gainsborough	
A/G	130.300	

Sumburgh

EGPB	civ South of Island (Hebrides)	
MET	125.725 (Scottish Volmet)	
ATIS	125.850	
APPROACH/RADAR	123.150	
TOWER	118.250	

Swansea

EGFH	civ 6 miles W of Swansea	
A/G/APPROACH	119.700	
TOWER	119.700	

Swanton Morley

EG	mil 4 miles N of Dereham (Norfolk)	
TOWER	123.500	

Swinderbury

EGXS	mil 8 miles NE of Newark (Lincs)	
APPROACH	283.425	
TOWER	122.100, 375.300	

Sywell see Northampton

Tatenhill

EGBM	civ 6 miles W of Burton-on-Trent	
A/G	122.200	

Teesside

EGNV	civ 6 miles E of Darlington	
MET	126.600 (London Volmet North)	
APPROACH	118.850	
TOWER	119.800	
VDF/RADAR	118.850, 119.800, 128.850	

Airfield

Ternhill   EG   mil 4 miles SW of Market Drayton
APPROACH   124.150, 122.100, 276.825, 362.300, 365.075
TOWER   124.150, 338.825, 309.550 (Chetwynd)
RADAR   123.300, 122.100, 344.375

Thruxton
EGHO   civ 6 miles W of Andover (Hants)
A/G   130.450

Tiree   EGPU   civ centre of island
AFIS   122.700)

Topcliffe   EGXZ   mil 4 miles SW of Thirsk (Yorkshire)
MATZ   Leeming
APPROACH   125.000, 121.100, 357.375, 362.300
TOWER   125.000, 121.100, 309.725, 257.800
SRE   123.300, 344.350, 385.400

Truro   EG   civ near town (Cornwall)
A/G   129.800

Unst   EGPW   civ Shetland Isles
APPROACH/TOWER   130.350

Upavon   EG   mil 8 miles N of Amesbury (Wilts)
TOWER   275.800

Upper Heyford
EGUA   mil 6 miles W of Bicester
ATIS   242.125
APPROACH   128.550, 123.300, 364.875
TOWER   122.100, 257.800, 316.000
GROUND   375.175
DISPATCHER   277.175
DEPARTURE   364.875
COMMAND POST   357.900, 359.850
METRO   257.750, 358.600
RADAR   128.550, 122.100
On standby for closure

Valley   EGOV   mil 6 miles SE of Hollyhead
MATZ   134.350, 268.775
SAR   282.800
APPROACH   134.350, 372.325, 362.300
TOWER   122.100, 340.175, 257.800
GROUND   122.100, 386.900
VDF   134.350
SRE   134.350, 123.200, 268.775, 282.800
DIRECTOR   337.725, 344.000
PAR   123.300, 358.675, 385.400

Airfield

Waddington
EGXW   mil 6 miles S of Lincoln
MATZ   127.350, 296.750
APPROACH   312.500, 362.300
TOWER   122.100, 285.050, 257.800
GROUND   342.125
DEPARTURE   123.300, 249.850
DISPATCHER   291.150
VDF   127.350
PAR   123.300, 309.675, 385.400
SRE   127.350, 123.300, 300.575, 344.000

Warton   EGNO   civ 4 miles E of Lytham/St Annes
APPROACH   124.450, 130.800, 336.475
TOWER   121.600, 130.800, 254.350
SRE   124.450, 130.800, 336.475, 254.350
RADAR   129.275, 343.700

Waterford
EIWF   civ Rebublic of Ireland
A/G/TOWER   129.850

Wattisham
EGUW   mil 10 miles NW of Ipswitch
APPROACH   135.200,
TOWER   122.100, 343.250
SRE   123.300, 277.475
PAR   123.300, 356.175, 359.825

Wellesbourne
EGBW   civ 4 miles E of Stratford-upon-Avon
A/G   130.450

Welshpool
EG   civ 12 miles W of Shrewsbury
A/G   123.250

West Freugh
EGOY   mil 4 miles SE of Stranraer
MATZ   130.050
APPROACH   130.050, 383.525
TOWER   122.550, 337.925
SRE   130.725, 383.525

West Malling
EGKM   civ 4 miles W of Maidstone
A/G   130.875

Westland Heliport
EGLW   civ Battersea (London)
TOWER   122.900

Airfield		
Weston	EIWT	civ Republic of Ireland
	A/G	122.400
Weybridge		
	EG	civ just S of town (Surrey)
	A/G	122.350
White Waltham		
	EGLM	civ 4 miles SW of Maidenhead
	A/G	122.600
Wick	EGPC	civ
	MET	118.300 (Kirkwall)
AFIS/APPROACH		119.700
	TOWER	119.700
Wickenby		
	EGNW	civ 10 miles NE of Lincoln
	A/G	122.450
Wigtown (Baldoon)		
	EG	civ Dumfries and Galloway
	A/G	123.050
Woodbridge		
	EGVG	mil 5 miles NE of Ipswitch
MATZ/APPROACH		See Bentwaters
	ATIS	336.000
	TOWER	119.150, 122.100, 257.800, 291.350
	GROUND	307.400
COMMAND POST		282.150
	METRO	259.400
Due for closure		
Woodford		
	EGCD	civ 4 miles E of Wilmslow (Lancs)
	APPROACH	130.050, 126.925, 269.125, 358.575
	TOWER	126.925, 130.050, 358.575, 299.975
	SRE	130.750, 130.050, 269.125, 358.575

Airfield		
Woodvale		
	EGOW	mil 6 miles SW of Southport (Lancs)
	APPROACH	122.100, 312.800
	TOWER	119.750, 259.950
Wroughton		
	EGDT	civ 3 miles S of Swindon
	A/G	123.225
Wycombe Air Park		
	EGTB	civ 3 miles SW of High Wycombe
	TOWER	126.550
	GROUND	121.775
Wyton	EGUY	mil 4 miles NE of Huntingdon
	MATZ	134.050
	APPROACH	134.050, 362.375, 362.300
	TOWER	122.100, 312.275, 257.800
	DEPARTURE	134.050, 375.525
	PAR	122.100, 292.900, 385.400
	SRE	123.300, 249.550, 344.000
Yeovil	EGHG	mil SW of town
	APPROACH	130.180, 369.975
	TOWER	125.400, 372.425
	SRE	130.800
	RADAR	127.350, 369.875
Yeovilton		
	EGDY	mil 2 miles E of Ilchester
	MATZ	127.350
	ATIS	379.750
	APPROACH	127.350, 369.875, 362.300
	TOWER	122.100, 372.650
	GROUND	311.325
	PAR	123.300, 339.975, 344.350
	SRE	123.300, 338.875, 362.300
	RADAR/VDF	127.350, 369.875

WHAT YOU MIGHT HEAR

Remember that aircraft transmissions are usually short and there may be long periods when nothing is heard on a frequency. This applies in particular to smaller airfields where traffic movement may be quite low. In addition to approach, control tower and radar landing instructions you may also hear a variety of other messages being passed on other frequencies in the bands. Many airlines have company frequencies on which aircraft crews and ground operation staff communicate. You may also hear transmissions relating to zone, area or sector controllers. These are the people who control the movements of aircraft as they fly between airports. Different sectors have different transmission frequencies and so, to follow a particular aircraft as it moves from one sector to another, you will need to change your reception frequencies to suit.

At London Heathrow and similar large airports, the sheer volume of traffic means that instructions passed to the aircraft must be done by several controllers and so you may come across frequencies which are dealing solely with such things as instructions on taxiing on the ground.

CONTINUOUS TRANSMISSIONS

Some frequencies are allocated solely for transmissions from the ground. The aircraft never transmit on these frequencies but the crews may listen to the broadcasts for information. The most common of these are VOLMETS, transmitted round the clock and detailing current weather conditions for most major airports. Automatic terminal information service (ATIS) transmissions on the other hand are sent out by individual airports and only include details of that airport, including current weather, runway and approach patterns in use, and any other essential information. They, in fact, contain all the information a pilot needs except actual landing permission. Pilots will listen to these transmissions and when contacting the controller will often be heard to say such things as 'information Bravo received' – the word Bravo standing for the code letter which identifies the start of an ATIS transmission.

RANGE

Using a reasonable outside aerial it may be possible to hear ground stations up to 20 miles or so away. However, if hills or large buildings are between the scanner and the airport then this range will be considerably reduced. For instance, in my own case I cannot pick up my local airport which is only four miles away and yet can pick up another airport which is some 25 miles away in a different direction.

Air-to-ground range though is a different matter altogether. Aircraft flying at tens of thousands of feet may be heard several hundred miles away even though the scanner is only operating on a small telescopic aerial. This is because the line-of-site range is greatly extended by the

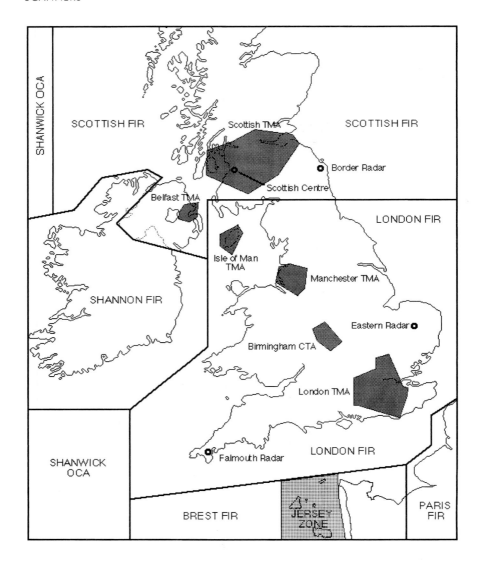

height of the aircraft which is transmitting from a point where there are no obstructions to block or weaken the signal. If an aerial is used solely for airband reception then it should be vertically polarised. It is worth noting, by the way, that a simple ground plane aerial of the type described in Chapter 5 is more than adequate for aircraft band-only operation. You will hear many unfamiliar expressions and considerable use of abbreviations in the airband. If you are not familiar with these, you can look them up in the airband section in Chapter 7.

Table 6.3 UK airways allocations

A/way	Sector	Control
A1	Turnberry & 54.30N	Scottish Ctl 126.250 & 128.500
	54.30N & abm Stafford	London Ctl 131.050, 129.100 & 134.425
	54.30N & abm Stafford	Manchester Ctl 126.650 & 124.210
	Abm Stafford & Birmingham	London Ctl 133.700, 134.425
	Abm Stafford & Birmingham	Manchester Ctl 124.200
	Birmingham & Abm Woodley	London Ctl 133.700 & 133.975
	Daventry area and Birmingham Zone Ctl	Birmingham SRA/SRZ 120.500
A2	TALLA & 54.30N	Scottish Ctl 128.500
	54.30N & Abm Lichfield	London Ctl 131.050 & 134.425
	54.30N & Abm Lichfield	Manchester Ctl 126.65 & 124.200
	Abm Lichfield & Abm Birmingham	London Ctl 121.025, 133.700 & 134.425
	Abm Lichfield & Abm Birmingham	Manchester Ctl 126.65 & 124.200
	Abm Birmingham & Brookmans Park	London Ctl 121.025, 133.700 & 133.975
	South of Brookmans Park	London Ctl 127.100 & 132.450
A20	FIR Boundary & Biggin	London Ctl 127.100
	Biggin & Abm Birmingham	London Ctl 121.025, 133.700 & 133.975
	Abm Birmingham & Pole Hill	London Ctl 131.050 above FL155
	Abm Birmingham & Pole Hill	Manchester Ctl 124.200 & 126.650
A25	Dean Cross & 54.30N	Scottish Ctl 126.250 & 128.500
	54.30N & REXAM	London Ctl 128.050, 129.100 & 134.425
	54.30N & REXAM	Manchester Ctl 133.050 & 125.100
	REXAM & Cardiff	London Ctl 131.200
	Cardiff & 50.00N	London Ctl 132.600 & 135.250
	50.00N & Channel Isles Boundary	Jersey Zone 125.200
A30	London FIR	London Ctl 127.100
A34	London FIR	London Ctl 127.700 & 124.275
A37	Entire route	London Ctl 129.600, 127.950, 133.450 & 133.525
A47	Pole Hill & Lichfied	London Ctl 131.050 above FLI55
	Pole Hill & Lichfield	Manchester Ctl 126.65, 124.200 below FL175
	Lichfield & abm Birmingham	London Ctl 133.700 Above FL135
	Lichfield & abm Birmingham	Manchester Ctl 124.200 below FL175
	Abm Birmingham & Woodley	London Ctl 133.700, 121.020
	Daventry CTA below FL130	London Ctl 133.975
	South of Woodley to FIR Boundary	London Ctl 127.700, 135.050 & 124.275
B1	West of Wallasey	London Ctl 128.050, 129.100 & 134.425
	West of Wallasey	Manchester Ctl 133.050 below FL175
	Wallasey & BARTN	London Ctl 128.050 & 134.425
	Wallasey & BARTN	Manchester Ctl 125.100 below FL175
	BARTN & Ottringham	London Ctl 131.050 & 134.425
	BARTN & Ottringham	Manchester Ctl 126.650 & 124.200
	East of Ottringham	London Ctl 134.250, 127.950 & 133.525
B2	North of TMA	Scottish Ctl 124.500
	South of TMA	Scottish Ctl 135.675
B3	Belfast & 5W	Scottish Ctl 135.675
	5W & Wallasey	London Ctl 128.050 & 129.100
	Wallasey & Stafford	London Ctl 128.050 & 129.100
	Wallasey & Stafford	Manchester Ctl 125.100 & 124.200

A/way	Sector	Control
	Stafford & abm Birmingham	London Ctl 133.7 & 121.025 above FL135
	Stafford & abm Birmingham	Manchester Ctl 125.1 & 124.200 below FL175
	Daventry CTA within A1	Birmingham Zone Ctl on 120.500 below FL80
	Abm Birmingham & Brookmans Park	London Ctl 133.700, 121.025 & 133.975
	South of Brookmans Park to FIR boundary	London Ctl 127.100 & 134.900
B4	Detling & Brookmans Park	London Ctl 127.100 & 134.900
	Brookmans Park & abm Birmingham	London Ctl 121.025, 133.700 & 133.975
	Abm Birmingham & ROBIN	London Ctl 121.025, 133.700 & 134.425 above FL135
	Abm Birmingham & ROBIN	Manchester Ctl 124.200 & 126.650 below FL175
	ROBIN & Pole Hill	London Ctl 131.050, 134.425 above FL155
	ROBIN & Pole Hill	Manchester Ctl 124.200 & 126.650 below FL175
	Pole Hill & 54.30N	London Ctl 131.050 & 134.425 above FL155
	Pole Hill & 54.30N	Manchester Ctl 126.65 124.200 below FL175
	54.30N & GRICE	Scottish Ctl 135.675 (night) & 128.500 (day)
B5	Entire route	London Ctl 134.250, 127.950 & 133.525
B11	Within London FIR	London Ctl 134.450, 127.700 & 124.275
B29	Within London FIR	London Ctl 129.600 & 127.950
B39	MALBY & RADNO	London Ctl 131.200
	RADNO & TOLKA	London Ctl 128.050
B53	Entire route	London Ctl 128.050 & 129.100 above FL155
	Entire route	Manchester Ctl 125.100 & 124.200 below FL175
B226	Entire route	Scottish Ctl 124.500
G1	West of Brecon	London Ctl 131.200
	Brecon & abm Woodley	London Ctl 132.800 & 131.200
	East of abm Woodley to FIR Boundary	London Ctl 134.900 & 127.100
G27	North of 50.00N	London Ctl 127.700 & 124.275R1
R1	ORTAC to Ockham	London Ctl 134.450, 132.300, 127.700 & 124.275
	Ockham to FIR Boundary	London Ctl 129.600, 127.950, 133.450 & 133.520
R3	Wallasey & ROBIN	London Ctl 128.050, 129.100 & 134.425 above FL155
	Wallasey & ROBIN	Manchester Ctl 125.100 & 124.200 below FL175
R8	BRIPO to Southampton	London Ctl 132.600 & 124.275
	Southampton to Midhurst	London Ctl 134.450, 132.300, 127.700 & 124.270
	Midhurst & Dover	London Ctl 134.900, 127.100 & 124.275
R12	Entire route	London Ctl 129.600, 127.950, 133.450 & 133.520
R123	Entire route	London Ctl 129.600, 127.950, 133.450 & 133.520
R14	Within London FIR	London Ctl 131.200
R25	Entire route	London Ctl 127.700
R41	ORTAC & Southampton	London Ctl 134.450, 132.300, 127.700 & 124.275
	Southampton & abm Compton	London Ctl 132.800, 131.200, & 124.275
	Abm Compton & Westcott	London Ctl 133.700 & 121.025
	Entire route	London Ctl 134.450, 132.300, 127.700 & 124.275
R126	Within London FIR	London Ctl 129.600 & 127.940
R803	Entire route	London Ctl 127.700 & 124.275
W1	Daventry to Abm Barkway	London Ctl 121.025, 133.700, & 133.975
	Abm Barkway to 20nm N of Dover	London Ctl 129.600, 127.950, & 133.450
	20nm North of Dover to Dover	London Ctl 132.900 & 127.100
W923	Entire route	London Ctl 131.050, 129.100, & 134.425 above FL155
	Entire route	Manchester Ctl 126.650 & 124.200 below FL175
W934	Within London FIR	London Ctl 127.700 & 124.275

A/way	Sector	Control
Lower ATS Advisory Routes		
A1D	60N 10W to Stornoway	Scottish Ctl 127.275
	Stornoway to Glasgow	Scottish Ctl 127.275
B1D	Within Scottish FIR	Scottish Ctl 131.300
G4D	Within London FIR	London Ctl 132.600
N552D	Entire route	Scottish Ctl 127.275
N562	Entire route	Scottish Ctl 127.275
N571D	Entire route	Scottish Ctl 127.275
R8D	Within London FIR	London Ctl 132.600
W2D	West of Fleetwood	London Ctl 128.050, 129.200, & 134.425 above FL155
	West of Fleetwood	Manchester Ctl 133.050 below FL175
	East of Fleetwood	London Ctl 131.050 & 134.425 above FL155
	East of Fleetwood	Manchester Ctl 126.650 & 124.200 below FL175
W3	South of Inverness	Scottish Ctl 124.500
	Between Inverness & Sumburgh	Scottish Ctl 131.300
W4D	Within Scottish FIR	Scottish Ctl 131.300
W5D	Within Scottish FIR	Scottish Ctl 131.300
W6D	Glasgow to Benbecula to Stornoway to 05.00W to Inverness	Scottish Ctl 127.275
W910D	Entire route	Scottish Ctl 127 275
W911D	South of 54.30N	Scottish Ctl 128.500 & Border Radar on 132.900
	South of 54.30N	London Ctl 128.050, 129.100, & 134.425 above FL155
	South of 54.30N	Manchester Ctl 133.050 below FL175
W927D	West of North light	London Ctl 128.050, 129.100 & 134.425 above FL 155
	West of North light	Manchester Ctl 133.050 below FL175
	East of North light	London Ctl 128.050, 134.425, above FL155
	East of North light	Manchester Ctl 133.050 below FL175
W928D	Entire route	Scottish Ctl 135.675
W985D	Entire route	Scottish Ctl 127.275
Upper ATS allocations		
UA1	North of 54.30N	Scottish Ctl 135.850
	Between 54.30N & abm Lichfield	London Ctl 131.050, 129.100 & 134.425
	Abm Lichfield & abm Woodley	London Ctl 133.700
	South of Woodley to UIR Boundary	London Ctl 127.700, 124.275 & 127.425
UA2	Machrihanish & 54.30N	Scottish Ctl 135.850
	54.30N & Trent	London Ctl 131.050, 129.100 & 134.425
	Trent & Lambourne	London Ctl 133.700 & 121.025
	South of Lambourne to UIR Boundary	London Ctl 127.100, 132.450 & 127.425
UA20	Entire route	London Ctl 127.100 & 127.425
UA25	GRICE to 54.30N	Scottish Ctl 135.850
	54.30N & South of Wallasey	London Ctl 128.050, 129.100 & 134.425
	South of Wallasey & S of Brecon	London Ctl 133.600
	South of Brecon to UIR	London Ctl 132.600, 131.050 Boundary 134.425
UA29	BAKUR & MERLY	London Ctl 133.600
	MERLY & SALCO	London Ctl 132.600
UA30	Entire route	London Ctl 127.100 & 127.425
UA34	Wallasey & TELBA	London Ctl 128.050 & 129.100
	TELBA & Abm Woodley	London Ctl 133.700

A/way	Sector	Control
	Abm Woodley & UIR Boundary	London Ctl 127.700, 124.270 & 127.425
UA37	DANDI & GABAD	London Ctl 134.250, 128.125 & 133.525
	GABAD & Detling	London Ctl 129.600, 127.950, 133.525 & 127.400
UA47	Daventry & Woodley	London Ctl 133.700 & 121.025
	South of Woodley to	London Ctl 127.700, 135.050, UIR Boundary 127.425
UA251	Pole Hill & TELBA	London Ctl 131.050 & 129.100
	TELBA & EXMOR	London Ctl 133.600
UB1	Liffey to Wallasey	London Ctl 128.050 & 134.425
	Wallasey to Ottringham	London Ctl 131.050 & 134.425
	East of Ottringham	London Ctl 134.250, 128.125 & 133.525
UB2	DALKY to Perth	Scottish Ctl 135.850, & 126.850
	Perth to KLONN	Scottish Ctl 124.050
UB3	Belfast to 05.00W	Scottish Ctl 135.85 & 126.850
	05.00W to 53.00N	London Ctl 128.050 & 121.025
	Brookmans Park & Dover	London Ctl 127.100, 134.900 & 127.425
UB4	FINDO & 54.30N	Scottish Ctl 135.850
	54.30N & ROBIN	London Ctl 131.050 & 134.425
	ROBIN & Brookmans Park	London Ctl 121.025 & 133.700
	South of Brookmans Park to UIR Boundary	London Ctl 127.100, 132.450 & 127.425
UB5	North of FAMBO	Scottish Ctl 135.850
	South of FAMBO	London Ctl 134.250, 128.125 & 133.525
UB10	Within London UIR	London Ctl 133.600
UB11	Within London UIR	London Ctl 134.450, 127 700, 124.275 & 127.400
UB29	Compton & Abm Brookmans Park	London Ctl 133.600 & 132.800
	East of Abm Brookmans Park to UIR Boundary	London Ctl 129.600, 127.950, 133.525 & 127.400
UB39	Midhurst & RADNO London	Ctl 133.600 & 132.600
	RADNO & TOLKA	London Ctl 128.050 & 127.425
UB40	Entire route	London Ctl 133.600 & 132.600
UB105	Within London UIR	London Ctl 134.250,128.125 & 133.525
UG1	West of Abm Woodley to UIR Boundary	London Ctl 133.600 & 132.800
	East of Abm Woodley to UIR Boundary	London Ctl 134.900, 127.100 & 127.425
UG4	Within London UIR	London Ctl 132.600
UG11	Within Scottish UIR	Scottish Ctl 124.050
UG106	Within London UIR	London Ctl 134.900, 127.100 & 127.425
UH71	Sumburgh to LIRKI	Scottish Ctl 124.050 & 134.775
UH73	GRICE to Machrihanish	Scottish Ctl 135.850 & 126.850
UL1	West of abm Woodley to UIR Boundary	London Ctl 133.600 & 132.800
	East of abm Woodley to UIR Boundary	London Ctl 134.900, 127.100 & 127.425
UL74	Entire route	London Ctl 134.250 & 128.125
UL7	North of SKATE	Scottish Ctl 124.050
	South of SKATE	London Ctl 134.250 & 128.125
UL722	Entire route	London Ctl 132.600 & 132.950
UN490	UIR Boundary to TAKAS	Brest Control 129.500
UN491	UIR Boundary to TAKAS	Brest Control 129.500
UN500	Entire route	London Ctl 132.600 & 132.950
UN508	UIR Boundary to TAKAS	Brest Control 129.500
UN510	RATKA to OMIMI	Shannon Ctl 135.600
UN520	OMIMI to UIR Boundary	Brest Ctl 129.5
UN549	Strumble to BAKUR	London Ctl 133.600 & 132 800

A/way	Sector	Control
UN550	ERNAN to 55.00N 01.00W	Scottish Ctl 135.850 & 126.850
UN551	Belfast to 55.00N 01.00W	Scottish Ctl 135.850 & 126.850
UN552	TALLA to Machrihanish to 55.00N 01.00W	Scottish Ctl 135.850 & 126.850 &
UN560	ERNAN to 55.00N 01.00W	Scottish Ctl 135.850
UN561	Belfast to 55.00N 01.00W	Scottish Ctl 135.850 & 126.850
UN562	Machrihanish to 55.00N 01.00W	Scottish Ctl 135.850 & 126.850
UN563	Glasgow to 55.00N 01.00W	Scottish Ctl 135.850 & 126.850
UN564	GRICE to 55.00N 01.00W	Scottish Ctl 135.850 & 126.850
UN570	GRICE to 56.00N 01.00W	Scottish Ctl 135.850 & 126.850
UN571	Machrihanish to 57.00N 01.00W	Scottish Ctl 135.850 & 126.850
UN572	Tiree to 57.00N 01.00W	Scottish Ctl 135.850 & 126.850
UN580	Glasgow to Tiree to 57.20N	Scottish Ctl 135.850 & 126.850
	57.20N to 58.00N 01.00W	Scottish 124.050 & 134.775
UN581	Aberdeen to Benbecula to 58.00N 01.00W	Scottish 124.050 & 134.775
UN582	ASPIT to 57.20N	Scottish Ctl 135.850 & 126.850
	57.20N to Stornoway	Scottish 124.050 & 134.775
UN58	Sumburgh to Stornoway to 58.00N 01.00W	Scottish Ctl 124.050 & 134.775
UN584	Sumburgh to 58.00N 01.00W	Scottish Ctl 124.050 & 134.775
UN590	MARGO to Glasgow & Benbecula	Scottish Ctl 135.850 & 126.850
	Benbecula to 59.00N 01.00W	Scottish Ctl 124.050 & 134.775
UN593	Sumburgh to 59.00N 01.00W	Scottish Ctl 124.050 & 134.775
UN601	TALLA to 57.20N	Scottish Ctl 135.850 & 126.850
	57.20N to Stornoway to 60.00N to 01.00W	Scottish Ctl 124.050 & 134.775
UN602	Glasgow to 57.20N	Scottish Ctl 135.850 & 126.850
	57.20N to RONAK to 60.00N	Scottish Ctl 124.050 & 134.775 & 01.00W
UN603	Sumburgh to 60.00N 01.00W	Scottish Ctl 124.050 & 134.775
UN610	Stornoway to 60.00N 01.00W	Scottish Ctl 124.050 & 134.775
UN611	BATSU to Aberdeen to RONAK to 60.10N 01.00W	Scottish Ctl 124.050 & 134.775
UN612	Sumburgh to 60.10N 01.00W	Scottish Ctl 124.050 & 134.775
UN615	Glasgow to 57.20N	Scottish Ctl 135.850 & 126.850
	57.20N to Stornoway to MATIK	Scottish Ctl 124.050 & 134.775
UR1	ORTAC/Midhurst to Lambourne	London Ctl 134.450, 127.700
UR12	abm Lambourne	132.300 & 124.275
UR123	Lambourne to Clacton to UIR Boundary	London Ctl 129.600, 127.950, 133.450, & 133.525 & 127.425
UR3	Entire route	London Ctl 128.050 & 134.425
UR4	IOM to Pole Hill	London Ctl 128.050 & 134.425
	Pole Hill to Ottringham	London Ctl 131.050 & 134.425
	Ottringham to DANDI	London Ctl 134.250, 128.125 & 133.525
UR8	From Land's End to Southampton	London Ctl 132.600, 124.275, 134.450, 132.300 & 127.700
	From Southampton to Midhurst	London Ctl 124.275 & 127.425
UR14	Within London UIR	London Ctl 132.600 & 133.600
UR23	Glasgow to SAB	Scottish Ctl 135.850
	SAB to GORDO	Scottish Ctl 124.050
UR24	ORIST to ASPEN	London Ctl 134.450, 132.300 & 127.700
UR25	Entire route	London Ctl 127.700 & 124.275
UR37	NORLA to Southampton	London Ctl 132.600 & 124.275
	Between Southampton & abm Midhurst	London Ctl 134.450, 127.700, 132.310 & 124.27
	Abm Midhurst to DONER	London Ctl 134.900, 127.100 124.275 & 127.425
UR38	Newcastle to 57.15N	Scottish Ctl 135.850 & 126.850

A/way	Sector	Control
	57.15N to Stornoway	Scottish Ctl 124.050 & 134.775
UR41	Between ORTAC & Southampton	London Ctl 134.450, 132.300 & 127.700
	Between Southampton & abeam Woodley	London Ctl 132.800 & 131.200
	Between Abm Woodley & Westcott	133.700, 121.025 & 127.425
UR84	ORTAC to Midhurst	London Ctl 132.300, 127.700 & 127.425
UR126	Entire route	London Ctl 129.600, 127.950 & 133.525
UR168	Land's End to CAVAL	London Ctl 132.600
UT7	From Land's End to NOTRO	London Ctl 132.600
	From NOTRO to ASKIL	Brest Ctl 129.500
UW1	Between Daventry & abm Barkway	London Ctl 121.025 & 133.700
	Between abm Barkway & Clacton	London Ctl 129.600, 127.950, 133.450 & 133.500
UW2	Between Compton & Brookmans Park	London Ctl 133.600, 132.600 & 127.425
Northern Radar Advisory Service area		
	North of W911D	Scottish Control 124.500
	South of W911D	Pennine Radar 128.675
Hebrides Upper Control Area		
	South of a line 57.30N 10.00W & TIR & 65.36N & 00.41W	Scottish Ctl 135.850 & 126.850
	North of a line 57.30N 10.00W & TIR & 65.36N & 00.41W	Scottish Ctl 124.050

NOTES ON CIVILIAN AIRPORT FREQUENCIES

Occasionally frequencies may be interchanged and, for instance, approach control will be handled by the tower. However, all the airfields shown do have their main frequencies listed. A/G (Air/Ground stations) are for the most part communication stations available at smaller airfields. Pilots can call these facilities to obtain current weather information and the operator may well also warn of any other aircraft that are in the circuit. However, unlike an air traffic controller, the operator is not licensed to give the pilot landing instructions and it is up to the pilot to keep a look-out and make sure that he is not going to endanger any other aircraft during landing or take-off.

MILITARY AIRPORT TRANSMISSIONS

Military airport transmissions use the same frequencies as civilian airports, but also have frequency allocations between 240 and 350 MHz.

These stations provide information on the military training areas closest to them. Training ranges are used for a variety of purposes including

Table 6.4 Special military allocations

Facility	Frequency (MHz)		Facility	Frequency (MHz)	
Aces High Ops (N Weald)	130.175		NATO low-level manoeuvres	273.900	
Boulmer Rescue	123.100		NATO SAR training	253.800	
Dalcross Tower (range)	122.600		Neatishead (range warning)	123.100	
Distress (army)	40.0500		SAR co-ordination air/sea	123.100	
Distress (including beacons)	243.000		Spadeadam Range	122.100	
Donna Nook Range	123.050		Standard Mil Field frequency	122.100	123.300
Lee-on-Solent rescue	132.650		Wembury Range control	122.100	
NATO emergency	243.000	40.050			

Table 6.5 UK military danger area activity information service (DAAIS)

Aberdeen	120.400	Donna Nook	123.050	Neatishead	123.100
Aberporth	122.150	Edinburgh	121.200	Newcastle	126.350
Bentwaters	119.000	Farnborough	125.250	Portland	124.150
Border Info	134.850	Goodwood	122.450	St. Mawgan	126.500
Border Info	132.900	Leeming	132.400	Salisbury Plain	130.150
Boscombe Down	126.700	Leuchars	126.500	Scottish Mil	124.900
Brawdy	124.400	Liverpool	119.850	Scottish Mil	133.200
Bristol	127.750	Llanbedr Radar	122.500	Train Range	118.900
Brize Radar	134.300	London Info	124.600	Waddington	127.350
Chivenor	130.200	London Info	134.700	Wembury Range	122.100
Culdrose	134.050	Lydd	120.700	West Freugh	130.050
Dalcross Tower	122.600	Lyneham	123.400	Yeovilton	127.350

gunnery on the ground, at sea and in the air. The airspace above the ranges is often closed to non-military aircraft and civilian pilots will call the above stations to determine whether or not they can fly through the areas.

MATZ stands for Military Aerodrome Traffic Zone and civilian aircraft are not allowed in these areas without permission. Calls to obtain permission will be made on the MATZ frequency shown. As with the civilian listing, many of the frequencies are interchangeable and it is not unusual for, say, the MATZ frequency to also be used for approach control or radar services.

MISCELLANEOUS AIRBAND SERVICES

In addition to general airport approach, take-off and landing services, there is a wide variety of other services. Aircraft need to be passed from one region to another and their use of designated airways needs to be controlled. When an aircraft is approaching London, for instance, it will have to change frequencies several times as it is handed from one sector to another. Crossing the borders of different countries also means a change of frequency to a new ground controller. Following an aircraft is easy as it is standard procedure in airband communication for the ground controller to tell the pilot which frequency to change to and for the pilot to repeat the frequency he has been given.

Emergency frequencies

Table 6.6 lists the allocated UK emergency frequencies and services. In addition to being allocated for emergency communications use, frequencies 121.5 MHz and 243.0 MHz are also used for search and rescue beacons of three forms. The first is a small transmitter emitting a radio bleep. It is triggered automatically when a crash occurs, or may be switched on manually. The second type contains a voice transmitter. The third type also includes a receiver, so turning it onto a full, two-way communications transceiver. These beacons are either handheld or, in the case of SARBE versions, fitted to lifejackets. Frequencies 156.0 MHz and 156.8 MHz (both marine frequencies) are used by search and rescue aircraft to communicate with lifeboats, etc.

Table 6.6 Emergency frequencies and services

Service	Frequencies (MHz)
Civilian	121.500
Boulmer Rescue	123.100–254.425–282.800–299.100
Leconfield Rescue	122.100–244.875–282.800
Lifeboat/coastguard	156.000 (FM)
Marine distress	156.800 (FM)
Military	243.000–40.0500
NATO (scene of search)	282.800
Search and rescue (air)	123.100

Navigational aids

Between the frequencies 108 MHz and 117.95 MHz you will hear a variety of navigational aids. These are VHF omni-range beacons (VOR) and instrument landing systems (ILS). Some of these services are paired with navigational aids on other bands to give additional services such as distance measuring (DME). Combined VOR/DME services are called VORTACS – the TAC part being a shortening of TACAN which in turn stands for 'tactical navigation'.

VOLMETS

These are transmit-only stations providing constantly updated weather information for a variety of major airports.

Table 6.7 VOLMETS providing weather information

Service	Frequency (MHz)
London VOLMET main	135.375
London VOLMET north	126.600
London VOLMET south	128.600
Dublin VOLMET	127.000
Scottish VOLMET	125.725

Table 6.8 Miscellaneous airband allocations

Service	Frequency (MHz)
Air-to-air	123.450
Air-to-air (North Atlantic only)	131.800
Balloons (hot air)	129.900
Distress	121.500
Fisheries protection surveillance	122.100 (North Sea)
	131.800 (SW approaches and Channel)
Fire vehicles	121.600
Gliders	130.100, 130.125, 130.400
Ground control	121.700, 121.800, 121.900
Hang gliders	129.900
Lighthouse helipads	129.700
Search and Rescue (SAR)	123.100

Table 6.9 Airline and handling agent frequencies

Operator	Frequency (MHz)		Operator	Frequency (MHz)		
Aceair	130.175		British Aerospace	123.050		
Aer Lingus	131.500	131.750	Beauport Aviation	129.700		
Air Atlantique	130.625		Britannia Airways	131.675		
Air Bridge Carriers	122.350		British Air Ferries	130.625		
Air Canada	131.450		British Airways	123.650	131.475	131.800
Air Foyle	131.775			131.550	131.625	131.850
Air France	131.500			131.900		
Air Hanson	130.375		British Island Airways	129.750		
Air India	131.600		British Midland	129.750	131.575	
Air Jamaica	131.450		British West Indian	131.450		
Air Kilroe	122.350		Brymon	123.650		
Air Malta	131.650		Channel Express	130.600		
Air UK	129.750	131.750	CSE Oxford	129.700		
Alitalia	131.450		Connectair	130.175		
Aurigny Aviation	122.350		Cyprus Airways	131.775		

Operator	Frequency (MHz)	Operator	Frequency (MHz)	
Danair	131.875	MAM	129.700	
Delta	130.600	Manx Airlines	129.750	
Diamond Air	129.700	MAS	131.575	
Eastern Airlines	131.900	McAlpine Aviation	123.650	
El Al	131.575	Monarch	131.525	
Eurojet	131.875	Nigerian Airways	131.775	
Execair	122.350	Northern	130.650	
Fields Heathrow	130.600	Pakistan International	131.450	
Finnair	131.950	Qantas	131.875	
Gatwick Handling	130.650	Royal Jordanian	131.425	
Genavco	130.375	Sabena	131.475	
Hatair	123.650	SAS	131.700	
Iberia	131.950	Saudia	131.425	
Inflight	130.625	Servisair	130.075	130.600
Interflight	130.575	Singapore Airlines	131.950	
Iran Air	131.575	Skycare	122.050	130.025
Japanese Airlines	131.650	Spurnair	122.050	
Jet centre	130.375	Swissair	131.700	
KLM	131.650	TAP	131.750	
Kuwait Airlines	131.500	Thai-Inter	131.450	
Loganair	130.650	TWA	131.600	
Lufthansa	131.925	Uni Avco	130.575	
Luxair	131.550	Veritair	129.900	
Magec	123.650	Wardair	129.700	

MARINE BAND

This, like the VHF airband, is one of the few international bands; it is common to *all* ITU regions. It is channelised in that radio equipment made for marine VHF use does not usually have facilities to tune to a given frequency, instead it has a channel selector which goes from channel 1 to channel 88. A list of marine band channels and their transmission frequencies is given in Table 6.10.

Channels are designated for specific uses in that some are for ship-to-shore use, others for ship-to-ship, and so forth. The method of operating on marine band is very different from airband. The use of GMDSS (Global Maritime Distress and Safety System) is employed in passenger-carrying and cargo vessels, where a non-speech DSC (Digital Selective Calling) transmission is initially made on channel 70, with a working channel allocated for subsequent speech communication. For other vessels, such as yachts and similar pleasure craft that may not be fully GMDSS equipped, there is a common calling frequency for speech: channel 16, at 156.8 MHz. When a ship wishes to call a another station, even though the operator may know the channel that is used by that shore station, he will normally make first contact on channel 16. Once contact is made either on channel 16 or via DSC on channel 70, the ship and shore station will then move to a working channel – in most instances this will be the station's prime channel for general transmissions, or link channel for link calls (i.e., ship-to-shore telephone calls). Channels 0 and 67 are used by lifeboats and the coast guard. Some search and rescue aircraft also have the facility to work these channels.

Table 6.10 shows that many channels have two frequencies – this is to enable duplex operation. Because these are duplex transmissions, it is impossible for a scanner to simultaneously monitor both frequencies. Two scanners would have to be used, each tuned to one of the two frequencies, if the whole transmission was to be received.

Range

The useful range for marine VHF communications tends to be somewhat better than for the same type of frequencies and power levels used across land. Quite simply, there are few obstructions at sea and maximum ranges of 50–100 miles are not unusual. However, while signals from a ship may be quite strong at a coastal station, the signals may deteriorate even a mile or two inland.

Table 6.10 International marine channels

Channel	Ship	Coast	Service
0	156.000		Coastguard/lifeboat
00	160.600		Coastguard/lifeboat
01	156.050	160.650	Port operations/link calls
02	156.100	160.700	Port operations/link calls
03	156.150	160.750	Port operations/link calls
04	156.200	160.800	Port operations/link calls
05	156.250	160.850	Port operations/link calls
06	156.300		Intership primary/search and rescue
07	156.350	160.950	Port operations/link calls
08	156.400		Intership
09	156.450		Intership
10	156.500		Intership/pollution control
11	156.550		Port operations
12	156.600		Port operations primary
13	156.650		Port operations
14	156.700		Port operations primary
15	156.750		Port operations
16	156.800		Calling channel
17	156.850		Port operations
18	156.900	161.500	Port operations
19	156.950	161.550	Port operations
20	157.000	161.600	Port operations

Channel	Ship	Coast	Service
21	157.050	161.650	Port operations
22	157.100	161.700	Port operations
23	157.150	161.750	Link calls
24	157.200	161.800	Link calls
25	157.250	161.850	Link calls
26	157.300	161.900	Link calls
27	157.350	161.950	Link calls
28	157.400	161.200	Link calls
29	157.450	162.050	Private channel
30	157.500	162.100	Private channel
31	157.550	162.150	Private channel
32	157.600	162.200	Private channel
33	157.650	162.250	Private channel
34	157.700	162.300	Private channel
35	157.750	162.350	Private channel
36	157.800	162.400	Private channel
37	157.850	162.450	Private channel
38	157.900	162.500	Private channel
39	157.950	162.550	Private channel
40	158.000	162.600	Private channel
41	158.050	162.650	Private channel
42	158.100	162.700	Private channel
43	158.150	162.750	Private channel
44	158.200	162.800	Private channel
45	158.250	162.850	Private channel
46	158.300	162.900	Private channel
47	158.350	162.950	Private channel
48	158.400	163.000	Private channel
49	158.450	163.050	Private channel
50	158.500	163.100	Private channel
51	158.550	163.150	Private channel
52	158.600	163.200	Private channel
53	158.650	163.250	Private channel
54	158.700	163.300	Private channel
55	158.750	163.350	Private channel
56	158.800	163.400	Private channel
60	156.025	160.625	Link calls
61	156.075	160.675	Link calls
62	156.125	160.725	Link calls
63	156.175	160.775	Link calls
64	156.225	160.825	Link calls
65	156.275	160.875	Link calls
66	156.325	160.925	Link calls
67	156.375		Intership/small yacht safety/coastguard
68	156.425		Intership
69	156.475		Intership
70	156.525		Digital Selective Calling/Distress
71	156.575		Port operations
72	156.625		Intership

Channel	Ship	Coast	Service
73	156.675		Intership/pollution control/Coastguard
74	156.725		Ports/lock keepers/swing bridges
77	156.875		Intership
78	156.925	161.525	Port operations
79	156.975	161.575	Port operations
80	157.025	161.625	Port operations
81	157.075	161.675	Port operations
82	157.125	161.725	Port operations
83	157.175	161.775	Port operations
84	157.225	161.825	Port operations
85	157.275	161.875	Port operations
86	157.325	161.925	Link calls
87	157.375	161.975	Link calls
88	157.425	162.025	calls calls
M1	157.850		Marinas
M2	161.675		Marinas & yacht clubs

On-board-ship UHF handset frequencies (FM-split frequency simplex)

CH1	457.525	paired with 467.525
CH2	457.550	paired with 467.550
CH3	457.575	paired with 467.675

Table 6.11 General marine services and channel allocations

Service	Channels
Ship-to-ship	6, 8, 9, 10, 13, 15, 17, 67, 68, 70, 72, 75, 76, 77, 78
Port operations (simplex)	9, 10, 11, 12, 13, 14, 15, 17, 67, 69, 71, 73, 74
Port operations (duplex)	1, 2, 3, 4, 5, 7, 18, 19, 20, 21, 22, 60, 61, 62, 63, 64, 65, 66, 78, 79, 80, 81, 82, 84
Public correspondence (link calls)	1, 2, 3, 4, 5, 7, 23, 24, 25, 26, 27, 28, 60, 61, 62, 63, 64, 65, 66, 82, 83, 84, 85, 86, 87, 88

SHORE STATIONS

Table 6.12 lists UK shore stations, together with their broadcast and working channels. All stations transmit local area navigation warnings (beacons out of action, hazardous floating objects, etc). Most, but not all, transmit local area weather forecasts and storm warnings.

Table 6.12 British and Irish coastal stations

	Traffic	Nav lists	Wx warn	Gale warn	
Cullercoats	0103	1303	0233		
Chs: 16 26	0303	1503	0633	0703	0303
	0503	1703	1033		0903
	0703	1903	1433		1503
	0903	2103	1833	1903	2103
	1103	2303	2233		
Hebrides	0103	1303	0203		
Chs: 16 26	0303	1503	0603	0703	0303
	0503	1703	1003		0903
	0703	1903	1403		1503
	0903	2103	1803	1903	2103
	1103	2303	2203		
Humber	0103	1503	0133		0303
Chs: 16 24 26 85	0303	1703	0533	0733	0903
	0503	1903	0933		1503
	0903	2103	1333		2103
	1103	2303	1733	1933	
	1303	2133			
Ilfracombe	0133	1533	0233		0303
Chs: 16 05 07	0533	1733	0633	0833	0933
	0733	1933	1033		1503
	0933	2133	1433		2103
	1133	2333	1833	2033	
	1333	2233			
Jersey	After wx		0433	0645	as req +
Chs: 16 82 25 67			0645	0745	
			0745	1245	
			0833	1845	0307
			1245	2245	0907
		1633	1845		1507
		2033	2245		2107
Land's End	0103	1503	0233		0303
Chs: 16 27 88 85 64	0303	1703	0633	0733	0903
	0503	1903	1033		1503
	0903	2103	1433		2103
	1103	2303	1833	1933	
	1303		2233		
Malin Head	0103	1503	0033		
Chs: 16 23 67 85	0503	1703	0433		
	0903	1903	0833		
	1103	2103	1233		
	1303	2303	1633		

	Traffic	Nav lists	Wx warn	Gale warn	
Niton	0103	1503	0233		0303
Chs: 16 04 28 81	0303	1703	0633	0733	0903
85 64 87	0503	1903	1033		1503
	0903	2103	1433		2103
	1103	2303	1833	1933	
	1303		2233		
North Foreland	0103	1503	0233		0303
Chs:16 05 26 66 65	0303	1703	0633	0733	0903
	0503	1903	1033		1503
	0903	2103	1433		2103
	1103	2303	1833	1933	
	1303		2233		
Portpatrick	0103	1303	0203		
Chs: 16 27	0303	1503	0603	0733	0303
	0503	1703	1003		0903
	0703	1903	1403		1503
	0903	2103	1803	1903	2103
	1103	2303	2203		
St Peter Port	After		0133		
Chs: 16 12 62 78	navigation	0533			
	warnings	0933			
			1333		
			1733		
			2133		
Shetland	0103	1303	0233		
Chs: 16 27	0303	1503	0633	0703	0303
Remote control	0503	1703	1033		0903
from Wick	0703	1903	1433		1503
	0903	2103	1833	1903	2103
	1103	2303	2233		
Stonehaven	0103	1303	0233		
Chs: 16 26	0303	1503	0633	0733	0303
	0503	1703	1033		0903
	0703	1903	1433		1503
	0903	2103	1833	1933	2103
	1103	2303	2233		
Valentia	0333	1533	0233		0033
Chs: 16 24 28 67	0733	1733	0633		
	0933	1933	1033		0633
	1333	2333	1833		1233
	2233	2033	1833		

Anglesey	Chs: 16 26 28 61 remote control by Portpatrick
Bacton	Chs: 16 07 63 64 03 remote control by Humber
Bantry	Chs: 16 23 67 85 remote control by Valentia
Belmullet	Chs: 16 67 83 remote control by Malin Head
Buchan	Chs: 16 25 87 remote control by Stonehaven
Cardigan Bay	Chs: 16 03 remote control by Portpatrick
Celtic	Chs: 16 24 remote control by Ilfracombe
Clyde	Chs: 16 26 remote control by Portpatrick
Collafirth	Chs: 16 24 remote control by Wick
Cork	Chs: 16 26 67 remote control by Valentia
Cromarty	Chs: 16 28 84 remote control by Wick
Dublin	Chs: 16 83 remote control by Malin Head
Forth	Chs: 16 24 62 remote control by Stonehaven
Glen Head	Chs: 16 24 67 remote control by Malin Head
Grimsby	Chs: 16 04 27 remote control by Humber
Hastings	Chs: 16 07 63 remote control by North Foreland
Islay	Chs: 16 25 60 remote control by Portpatrick
Lewis	Chs: 16 05 remote control by Stonehaven
Mine Head	Chs: 16 67 83 remote control by Valentia
Morcambe Bay	Chs: 16 04 82 remote control by Portpatrick
Orfordness	Chs: 16 62 82 remote control by North Foreland
Orkney	Chs: 16 26 remote control by Wick
Pendennis	Chs: 16 62 66 remote control by Land's End
Rosslare	Chs: 16 23 67 remote control by Valentia
Shannon	Chs: 16 24 28 67 remote control by Valentia
Skye	Chs: 16 24 remote control by Stonehaven
Start Point	Chs: 16 26 65 60 remote control by Land's End
Thames	Chs: 16 02 83 remote control by North Foreland
Weymouth Bay	Chs: 16 05 remote control by Niton
Whitby	Chs: 16 25 28 remote control by Cullercoats
Wick	See Shetland

*Remote stations broadcast at the same time as their control stations.

Table 6.13 Ports, harbours and marinas in Great Britain

Port/Harbour	Channels	Port/Harbour	Channels
Aberdeen (Aberdeen)		**Abersoch** (Gwynedd)	
Aberdeen Radio	10 11 12 13 16	South Caernarfon Yacht Club	37 80
Aberdovey (Gwynedd)		**Aberystwyth** (Dyfed)	
Aberdovey Harbour	12 16	Harbour Control	14 16

Port/Harbour	Channels
Alderney see Braye	
Amble (Northumberland)	
Amble Harbour	14 16
Amble Braid Marina	37 80
Appledore (Devon) see River Taw	
Ardrishaig (Argyll)	
Harbour	16 74
Avonmouth (Avon) see Bristol	
Barmouth (Gwynedd)	
Barmouth Harbour	10 16
Barry (South Glamorgan)	
Barry Radio	10 12
Beaucette (Guernsey)	
Marina	16 37 80
Bembridge (Isle of Wight)	
Bembridge Marina	16 37 80
Berwick-on-Tweed (Northumberland)	
Pilots and Harbourmaster	12 16
Blackwater River (Essex)	
Bradwell & Tollesbury Marinas	37 80
Blyth (Northumberland)	
Blythe Harbour Control	12 16
Boston (Lincolnshire)	
Boston Dock	12
Grand Sluice	74
Braye (Alderney)	
Alderney Radio	16 74
Mainbryce Marina (summer only)	37 80
Bridlington (Humberside)	
Bridlington Harbour	12 14 16
Bridport (Dorset)	
Bridport Radio	11 12 14 16
Brighton (East Sussex)	
Brighton Control	11 16 68
Marina	37 80

Port/Harbour	Channels
Bristol (Avon)	
Avonmouth Radio	12
South Pier & Royal Edward Dock	12
Port Operations	09 11 14 16
Pilots	06 08 09 12 14
Royal Portbury, Portishead & City Docks	12 14 16
Floating Harbour	16 73
Newport	09 11 16
Brixham (Devon)	
Harbour	14 16
Pilots	09 10 13 16
Brixham Coastguard	10 16 67 73
Bude (Cornwall)	
Bude Radio	12 16
Burghead (Moray)	
Harbour	14 16
Burnham-on-Crouch (Essex)	
Essex and West Wick Marinas	37 80
Burnham-on-Sea (Somerset)	
Harbour Master and Pilots	08 16
Watchet	09 12 14 16
Marina	37 80
Caernarfon (Gwynedd)	
Caernarfon Radio (day only)	12 14 16
Caledonian Canal (Inverness) see also Inverness	
All locks	74
Campbeltown (Argyll)	
Harbour	12 14 16
Cardiff (South Glamorgan)	
Docks	11 14 16
Marina	37 80
Cattewater Harbour (Devon) see Plymouth-Devonport	
Charlestown (Cornwall) see Fowey	
Chichester (West Sussex)	
Harbour	14 16
Marinas	37 80
Colchester (Essex)	
Colchester Harbour Radio	11 14 16

Port/Harbour	Channels
Conwy (Gwnedd)	
Conway	06 08 12 14 16 72
Llanddulas	14 16
Cruising Club	37 80
Cowes (Isle of Wight)	
Cowes	06 11 16
Island Harbour and marinas	37 80
Chain Ferry	10
Craobh Haven/Loch Shuna (Argyll)	
Marina	16 37 80
Crinan (Argyll)	
Harbour	16 74
Cromarty Firth see Inverness	
Dartmouth (Devon)	
Harbour/Pilots	14
Dart Marina & Sailing Centre	37 80
Kingswear Marina ('Marina Four')	37 80
Fuel barge	16
Water taxi	16 37 80
Devonport (Devon) see Plymouth-Devonport	
Douglas (Isle of Man)	
Douglas Harbour	12 16
Dover (Kent)	
Dover Port Control	12 74
Channel Navigation Information Service	11 16 67 69 80
Information broadcasts (H+40)	11
Dundee/River Tay (Fife/Angus)	
Dundee Harbour Radio	10 11 12 13 14 16
Perth Harbour	09
East Loch Tarbert (Argyll)	
Harbour	16
Exeter (Devon)	
Harbour	06 12 16
Pilots	09 12 14 16
Eyemouth (Berwick)	
No regular watch	12 16
Falmouth (Cornwall) see also River Fal	
Falmouth Harbour Radio	11 16

Port/Harbour	Channels
Felixstowe (Suffolk) see Harwich	
Firth of Forth (Lothian Fife)	
North Queensferry Naval Station	13 16 71
Rosyth Naval Base ('QHM')	13
Forth Navigation Service	12 16 20 71
Grangemouth Docks	14 16
Port Edgar Marina	37 80
BP Grangemouth Terminal	14 16 19
Braefoot Terminal	15 16 69 73
Hound Point Terminal	09 10 12 16 19
Fishguard (Dyfed)	
Fishguard Radio	14 16
Marina	37 80
Fleetwood (Lancashire)	
Fleetwood Harbour Control	11 12 16
Fleetwood Docks	12 16
Ramsden Docks	12 16
Folkestone (Kent)	
Harbour	16 22
Pilot Station	09
Fowey (Cornwall)	
Fowey Harbour Radio	12 16
Pilots	09
Water taxi	06
Boat Marshall Patrol	12 16
Charlestown	14 16
Par Port Radio	12 16
Fraserburgh (Aberdeen)	
Harbour	12 16
Glasson Dock (Lancashire)	
Glasson Radio	08 16
Marina	M
Gorey (Jersey)	
Gorey Harbour (summer only)	74
Gravesend (Essex)	
Gravesend Radio	12 16
Great Yarmouth (Norfolk)	
Yarmouth Radio	09 11 12 16
Breydon Bridge	12
Greenock (Renfrew)	
Clydeport Estuary Radio	12 14 16
Dunoon Pier	12 16 31

Port/Harbour	Channels
Grimsby (Humberside)	
see also River Humber	
Grimsby (Royal Dock)	09 16 18
Guernsey	
see St Peter Port, St Sampsons & Beaucette	
Hamble (Hampshire)	
Hamble Harbour Radio	16 68
Marinas	37 80
Hartlepool (Cleveland)	
Hartlepool Dock Radio	11 12 16
Harwich (Essex)	
Harwich Harbour Control	11 14 16 71
Harbour Board patrol launch	11
Shotley Poin Marina	37 80
Havengore (Essex) see Shoeburyness	
Helensburgh (Dumbarton)	
Rhu Marina	37 80
Faslane (nuclear sub base) Patrol Boats	16
Helford River (Cornwall)	
Helford River SC & Gweek Quay	37 80
Marina	
Heysham (Lancashire)	
Heysham	14 16
Holyhead (Gwynedd)	
Holyhead Radio	14 16
Anglesey Marine Terminal	10 12 16 19
Ilfracombe (Devon)	
Ilfracombe Harbour (summer only)	12 16 37 80
Immingham (Humberside)	
see also River Humber	
Immingham Docks	09 16 22
Inverkip (Renfrew)	
Kip Marina	37 80
Inverness (Inverness)	
Inverness Harbour Office	06 12 14 16
Inverness Boat Centre & Caley Marina	37 80
Cromarty Firth Port Control	06 08 11 12 13 14 16
Clachnaharry Sea Lock & Caledonian Canal	74

Port/Harbour	Channels
Ipswich (Suffolk)	
Ipswich Port Radio	12 14 16
Marinas and yacht harbour	37 80
Isle of Man see also I.O.M. ports	
Radio/Landline link to Liverpool	12 16
Isles of Scilly	
Land's End Radio	64
St Mary's Harbour	14 16
Jersey see St Helier & Gorey	
King's Lynn (Norfolk)	
King's Lynn Radio	11 14 16
Docks	11 14 16
Wisbech	09 14 16
Kirkcudbright (Kirkcudbrightshire)	
Harbour	12 16
Kirkwall (Orkney Islands)	
Kirkwall Radio	12 16
Orkney Harbour Radio	09 11 16 20
Langstone (Hampshire)	
Langstone	12 16
Marina	37 80
Largs (Ayr)	
Yacht Haven	37 80
Lerwick (Shetland Islands)	
Lerwick	11 12 16
Sullom Voe	12 14 16 19 20
Scalloway	12 16
Balta Sound (no regular watch)	16 20
Littlehampton (West Sussex)	
Littlehampton	14 16
Marina	37 80
Liverpool (Merseyside)	
Mersey Radio	09 12 16 18 19 22
Alfred & Gladstone Docks	05
Tranmere Stages	09
Gartson & Waterloo Docks	20
Langton Dock	21
Eastham Locks (Manchester Ship Canal)	07 14
Latchford Locks (Manchester Ship Canal)	14 20
Weaver Navigation & Weston Point	74
Marsh, Dutton & Saltisford Locks	74
Anderton Depot	74

Port/Harbour	Channels
Loch Craignish (Argyll)	
Yachting Centre	16 37 80
Loch Maddy (North Uinst)	
Harbour	12 16
Loch Melfort (Argyll)	
Camus Marine	16 37 80
London see River Thames	
Looe (Cornwall)	
Only occasional watch	16
Lossiemouth (Moray)	
Lossiemouth Radio	12 16
Lowestoft (Suffolk)	
Harbour	14 16
Pilots	14
Lyme Regis (Dorset)	
Lyme Regis Harbour Radio	14 16
Lymington (Hampshire)	
Marinas	37 80
Lulworth Gunnery Range (Dorset)	
Range Safety Boats	08
Portland Naval Base	13 14
Portland Coastguard	67
Macduff (Banff)	
Harbour	12 16
Mallaig (Inverness)	
Mallaig Harbour Radio	09 16
Manchester (Lancashire)	
Ship canal	14 16
Barton & Irlham Docks & Mode Wheel Lock	14 18
Stanlow Oil Docks & Latchford Lock	14 20
Eastham Lock	07 14
Tugs inbound	08
Tugs outbound	10
Weaver Navigation Service	14 71 73
Maryport (Cumbria)	
Maryport Harbour (occasional watch)	12 16
Methil (Fife)	
Methil Radio	14 16

Port/Harbour	Channels
Mevagissey (Cornwall)	
Harbour	16 56
Milford Haven (Dyfed)	
Milford Haven Radio	09 10 11 12 14 16 67
Patrol & Pilot launches	06 08 11 12 14 16 67
Milford Docks	09 12 14 16
Amoco/Gulf Terminals	14 16 18
Esso Terminal	14 16 19
Texaco Terminal	14 16 21
Marina and Yacht Station	37 80
Minehead (Somerset)	
Minehead Radio (occasional watch only)	12 14 16
Montrose (Angus)	
Montrose Radio	12 16
Newhaven (East Sussex)	
Harbour	12 16
Marina	37 80
Newlyn (Cornwall)	
Newlyn Harbour	12 16
Pilots	09 12 16
Newquay (Cornwall)	
Newquay Radio	14 16
North Shields (Tyne and Wear) see River Tyne	
Oban (Argyll)	
Coastguard	16
Padstow (Cornwall)	
Padstow Radio	16 14
Par Port Radio (Cornwall) see Fowey	
Peel (Isle of Man)	
Peel	12 16
Penzance (Cornwall)	
Harbour/Pilots	09 12 16
Peterhead (Aberdeen)	
Peterhead Radio	09 11 14 16

Port/Harbour	Channels
Plymouth – Devonport (Devon)	
Long Room Port Control	08 12 14 16
Mill Bay Docks	12 14 16
Sutton Harbour Radio	12 16 37 80
Marinas, Yacht harbour & Clubs	37 80
Cattewater Harbour Office	12 16
Poole (Dorset)	
Poole Harbour Control	14 16
Pilots	06 09 14 16
Salterns Marina ('Gulliver Base')	37 80
Cobb's Quay	37 80
Porthmadog (Caernarfon)	
Harbour Master	12 16
Madoc Yacht Club	16 37
Portland (Dorset)	
Portland Naval Station	13 14
Portland Coastguard	16 67 69
Port of London	see River Thames
Portpatrick (Wigtown)	
Portpatrick Coast Radio Station	16 27
Stranraer	14 16
Portree (Skye)	
Port (no regular watch)	08 16
Port Saint Mary (Isle of Man)	
Port Saint Mary Harbour	12 16
Portsmouth (Hampshire)	
see also Solent	
Portsmouth Harbour Radio	11 13
Queens Harbour Master	11
Portsmouth Naval	13
Marina ('Camper Base' & yacht harbour)	37 80
Fort Gilkicker	16
Ramsey (Isle of Man)	
Ramsey	12 16
Ramsgate (Kent)	
Harbour & Marina	14 16
River Avon	see Bristol
River Deben (Suffolk)	
Tide Mill Yacht Harbour	37 80
Pilot	08

Port/Harbour	Channels
River Exe (Devon)	
Exeter	06 12 16
River Fal (Cornwall)	
Falmouth Harbour Radio	11 16
Pilots	06 08 09 10 11 12 14 16
Coastguard	10 16 67 73
Customs Launch	06 09 12 16
Port Health	06 12 16
Yacht harbour, marina and club	37 80
River Humber (Humberside)	
Humber Vessel Traffic Service	12 16
Grimsby (Royal Dock)	09 16 18
Immingham Docks	09 16 22
River Hull Port Operations ('Drypool Radio')	06 14 16
Tetney Oil Terminal	16 19
Goole Docks	14 16
Booth Ferry Bridge	12 16
Selby Bridges	09 12 16
Marinas and yacht harbour	37 80
River Medway (Kent)	
see also The Swale	
Medway Radio	09 11 16 22 74
Marinas	37 80
River Ore (Suffolk)	
Orford	16 67
River Orwell (Suffolk)	
see Ipswitch	
River Taw (Devon)	
Pilots	06 09 12 16
River Tees (Cleveland)	
Tees Harbour Radio	08 11 12 14 16 22
River Thames (London)	
Woolwich Radio	14 16 22
Gravesend Radio	12 14 16 18 20
Thames Radio	02
Thames Patrol	06 12 14 16
Thames Barrier	14
Thames Navigation Service	12
St Katherines Yacht Haven	37 80
Chelsea Harbour Marina	14 16 37
Brentford Dock Marina	14 16
North Foreland	26
Hastings	07
Orfordness Radio	62
Shellhaven	16 19

Port/Harbour	Channels
River Tyne (Tyne and Wear)	
Tyne Harbour Radio	11 12 14 16
Rona Naval Base (Rona)	
Base	16
Rothesay (Isle of Bute)	
Harbour	12 16
Rye (East Sussex)	
Harbour	14 16
Saint Helier (Jersey)	
Saint Helier Port Control	14
Jersey Radio	16 25 82
Lifeboat	00 16 14
Saint Kilda (Saint Kilda Island)	
Kilda Radio	08 16
Saint Peter Port (Guernsey)	
Port Control	12 16 21
Lifeboat	00 12 16
Saint Sampsons (Guernsey)	
Harbour	12 16
Salcombe (Devon)	
Salcombe Harbour	14
ICC Clubhouse & Floating HQ	37 80
Fuel barge	06
Water taxi	14
Scarborough (North Yorkshire)	
Scarborough Lighthouse	12 14 16
Scrabster (Caithness)	
Harbour	12 16
Seaham (Durham)	
Seaham Harbour	06 12 16
Sharpness (Gloucestershire)	
Sharpness Control	14 16
Bridges	74
Sheerness (Kent) see River Medway	
Shetland Islands	
Shetland Radio	16 27
Collafirth Radio	16 24
Shoeburyness (Essex)	
Gunnery Range Operations Officer	16
Gravesend Radio	12

Port/Harbour	Channels
Shoreham (West Sussex)	
Marinas	37 80
Solent (Hampshire)	
Solent Coastguard	00 06 10 16 67 73
Southampton Port Radio	12 14 16 18 20 22
Pilots	06 08 09 10 12 14 16 18
Queen's Harbour Master (Portsmouth)	11 13
Commercial Harbour Master (Portsmouth)	11
Pilots	09
Ships, tugs, & berthing	71 74
BP Terminal	06 16 18
Esso Terminal	14 16 18
Southampton (Hampshire) see also Solent	
Vessel Traffic Services	12 14 16
Harbour Patrol	10 12 14 16 18 22 71 74
Marinas	37 80
Southwold (Suffolk)	
Southwold Port Radio	12 16
Pilots	09 12
Stornoway (Outer Hebrides-Lewis)	
Harbour	12 16
Stromness (Orkney Islands)	
Stromness Radio	12 16
Sullom Voe	see Lerwick
Sunderland (Tyne and Wear)	
Sunderland Docks	14 16
Sutton Harbour (Devon) see Plymouth-Devonport	
Swansea (West Glamorgan)	
Swansea Docks Radio	14 16
Marina	37 80
Teignmouth (Devon)	
Harbour/Pilots	12 16
Tenby (Dyfed)	
Listening watch days only	16
The Swale (Kent)	
Medway Radio	09 11 16 22 74
Kingsferry Bridge	10
Torquay (Devon)	
Harbour	14 16

Port/Harbour	Channels	Port/Harbour	Channels
Troon (Ayr)		**Whitby** (North Yorkshire)	
Marina	37 80	Whitby Harbour	11 12 16
Androssan	12 14 16	Whittby Bridge	06 11 16
Girvan	12 16		
		Whitehills (Banff)	
Ullapool (Ross and Cromarty)		Whitehills Harbour Radio	09 16
Port	12 16		
		Whitstable (Kent)	
Watchet (Somerset)		Harbour	09 12 16
Port/Pilots	09 12 14 16		
		Wick (Caithness)	
Wells-next-the-Sea (Norfolk)		Harbour	14 16
Wells Radio	06 08 12 16		
		Wisbech (Cambridgeshire)	
Weymouth (Dorset)		Wisbech Cut	09 14 12
Harbour	12 16		
Pilots	09 16	**Workington** (Cumbria)	
		Workington Docks	14 16

Principal simplex allocations

Table 6.14 lists principal simplex services' allocated channels.

Table 6.14 Principal simplex services' channel allocations

Service	Channel
Calling and distress	16
Port operations (prime)	12
Port operations (alternative)	14
Small yacht safety	67
Marinas	M/M2
Intership (prime)	06
Intership (alternative)	08

AMATEUR BANDS

Most general-purpose scanners will cover at least one of the VHF/UHF amateur bands. Although many scanner users may look to such things as air and marine bands as being the more exciting listening, amateur bands do have an attraction in that the operators are not subject to the same power restrictions, and so even at VHF and UHF amateur radio becomes international in its coverage. During the summer months, in particular, effects such as sporadic-E and tropospheric ducting can mean that signals can be picked up over several hundreds of miles.

British amateurs are restricted at VHF and UHF to five bands: 6 metre, 4 metre, 2 metre, 70 centimetres and 23 centimetres. There are other bands but these are beyond the coverage of most scanners.

6 metre band

This particular band is also available to amateurs in countries in Regions 2 and 3 (including the USA). There the band lies between 50–54 MHz and many amateurs claim that because it is lower in frequency than 2 metre and 4 metre bands it should be possible at times at achieve very good distances. The Gibraltar beacon for example ZB2 VHF, on 50.035 MHz, is regularly heard in Britain. Transatlantic communications have also been achieved, at these frequencies, in the past.

Table 6.15 Recommended UK frequency allocations in the 6 metre band

Frequency	(MHz) Allocation
50.000–50.100	CW only
	50.020–50.080 MHz – beacons
50.100–50.500	SSB and CW only
	50.110 MHz Intercontinental calling
50.500–51.000	All modes
	50.710–50.910 FM repeater outputs in 10 kHz steps
51.000–52.000	All modes
	51.210–51.410 FM repeater inputs (mobile Tx)
51.430–51.830	FM simplex channels in 20 kHz steps
	51.510 FM simplex calling channel
51.830–52.00	All modes (emergency communications priority)

Table 6.16 Recommended UK frequency allocations in the 4 metre band

Frequency (MHz)	Allocation
70.000–70.030	Beacons
	70.030 MHz – personal beacons
70.030–70.250	SSB and CW only
	70.200 MHz – SSB and CW calling
70.250–70.300	All modes
	70.260 MHz – AM/FM calling
70.300–70.500	Channelised operation in 12.5 kHz steps
	70.3125, 70.3250, 70.3375 MHz – packet radio
	70.3500, 70.3750, 70.4000 MHz – emergency communications priority
	70.4500 MHz – FM calling
	70.4875 MHz – packet radio

4 metre band

This band is one of the least used by amateurs, although it is actively used for packet digital communications as well as various amateur emergency communication groups. Possibly one reason why it is not popular is that Britain is one of the few countries in the world with an allocation at these frequencies and so little if any international working is possible. The band extends from 70.025 to 70.5 MHz and the only allocations are as given in Table 6.16.

2 metre band

This is without a doubt the most popular amateur VHF band and signals can usually be heard on it in most areas at any time of day. The UK band extends from 144–146 MHz but in other regions the band is extended even higher. Equipment for this band is relatively cheap and portable which makes it a favourite with amateurs for local contact work.

Range on the band varies enormously but these varying conditions can mean that a transmission of several hundred watts output may only be heard 20 or 30 miles away at one time, while a signal of a few watts could be picked up hundreds of miles away at another time. Peak propagation tends to be in the summer when sporadic-E activity is at its highest. The band is used for a whole range of transmission types and several modes are used. Frequency allocation, listed in Table 6.17, is more by a sort of gentlemen's agreement than anything else. The band is organised into blocks of transmission types.

The abbreviation MS, used in Table 6.17, stands for 'meteor scatter', a method of reflecting a radio signal off the tail of a meteor or a meteor shower. A similar method of communication is involved in 'moon-bounce'. These types of communications are generally beyond the scope of scanner users as highly sensitive equipment and massive aerial arrays are required. FM channelised simplex and repeater activity uses 12.5 kHz spacing on this band although the majority of FM speech activity can be found on 25 kHz spaced steps.

70 centimetre band

This band is allocated between 430.00 and 440 MHz. It is allocated on a secondary basis which means that amateurs using it must not interfere with services on the band. Other users include PMR in the London area in the 431-432 MHz segment, and military users across the range who have primary status in this band. Short-range unprotected low-power telemetry devices, including some car key fobs, operate around 433.920 MHz.

The characteristics of the band are very similar to those of the 2 metre band with the exception that operators do not get the extreme ranges

Table 6.17 UK frequency allocations on the 2 metre band

Frequency	(MHz) Allocation
144.000–144.150	CW only
	144.000–144.030 MHz – moonbounce
	144.050 MHz – CW calling
	144.100 MHz – CW MS reference freq.
	144.140-144.150 – CW FAI working
144.150–144.500	SSB and CW only
	144.150–144.160 MHz – SSB FAI working
	144.195–144.205 MHz – SSB random MS
	144.250 MHz – used for slow Morse transmissions and weekend news broadcasts
	144.260 MHz – emergency comms priority
	144.300 MHz – SSB calling frequency
	144.390–144.400 MHz – SSB random MS
144.500–144.800	All modes non-channelised
	144.500 MHz – SSTV calling
	144.575 – ATV talkback (SSB)
	144.700 MHz – FAX calling
	144.750 MHz – ATV calling and talkback
	144.775–144.800 MHz – emergency communications priority
144.800–144.990	Digital modes
145.000–145.1875	FM repeater inputs
145.2000–145.5875	FM simplex channels
	145.2000 MHz – V16 (S8) emergency communications priority
	145.2250 MHz – V18 (S9) emergency communications priority
	145.2500 MHz – V20 (S10) used for slow Morse transmissions
	145.2750 MHz – V22 (S11)
	145.3000 MHz – V24 (S12) RTTY/AFSK
	145.3250 MHz – V26 (S13)
	145.3500 MHz – V28 (S14)
	145.3750 MHz – V30 (S15)
	145.4000 MHz – V32 (S16)
	145.4250 MHz – V34 (S17)
	145.4500 MHz – V36 (S18)
	145.4750 MHz – V38 (S19)
	145.5000 MHz – V40 (S20) FM calling channel
	145.5250 MHz – V42 (S21) used for weekend news broadcasts
	145.5500 MHz – V44 (S22) used for rally and exhibition talk-in
	145.5750 MHz – V46 (S23)
145.6000–145.7875	FM repeater outputs
	145.6000 MHz – RV48 (R0) 145.7000 MHz – RV56 (R4)
	145.6125 MHz – RV49 145.7125 MHz – RV57
	145.6250 MHz – RV50 (R1) 145.7250 MHz – RV58 (R5)
	145.6375 MHz – RV51 145.7325 MHz – RV59
	145.6500 MHz – RV52 (R2) 145.7500 MHz – RV60 (R6)
	145.6625 MHz – RV53 145.7625 MHz – RV61
	145.6750 MHz – RV54 (R3) 145.7750 MHz – RV62 (R7)
	145.6875 MHz – RV55 145.7875 MHz – RV63
145.8000–146.0000	Satellite service

achieved at times on the 2 metre band. By and large the band is less used than the 2 metre band although in densely populated areas there can be a fairly high level of activity. Like the 2 metre band, the 70 centimetre band also has repeaters, throughout the country, which considerably increase the range of operation. Frequency allocations, again divided into blocks of transmission types, are listed in Table 6.18.

Table 6.18 Recommended UK frequency allocations in the 70 centimetre band

Frequency (MHz)	Allocation
430.000–432.000	All modes (431–432 MHz is used for PMR in the London Area)
	430.810–430.990 low-power repeater inputs
432.000–432.150	CW only
	423.000–432.025 MHz – moonbounce
	432.050 MHz – CW centre of activity
432.150–432.500	SSB and CW only
	432.200 MHz – SSB centre of activity
	432.350 MHz – Microwave talkback
432.500–432.800	All modes non-channelised
	432.500 MHz – SSTV activity centre
	432.600 MHz – RTTY FSK activity centre
	432.625, 432.650, 432.675 MHz – packet radio
	432.700 MHz – FAX activity centre
432.800–432.990	Beacons
433.000–433.3875	FM repeater outputs
	433.000 MHz – RU240 (RB0) 433.200 MHz – RU256 (RB8)
	433.025 MHz – RU242 (RB1) 433.225 MHz – RU258 (RB9)
	433.050 MHz – RU244 (RB2) 433.250 MHz – RU260 (RB10)
	433.075 MHz – RU246 (RB3) 433.275 MHz – RU262 (RB11)
	433.100 MHz – RU248 (RB4) 433.300 MHz – RU264 (RB12)
	433.125 MHz – RU250 (RB5) 433.325 MHz – RU266 (RB13)
	433.150 MHz – RU252 (RB6) 433.350 MHz – RU268 (RB14)
	433.175 MHz – RU254 (RB7) 433.375 MHz – RU270 (RB15)
433.400–434.600	FM simplex channels
	433.400 MHz – U272 (SU16)
	433.425 MHz – U274 (SU17)
	433.450 MHz – U276 (SU18)
	433.475 MHz – U278 (SU19)
	433.500 MHz – U280 (SU20) FM calling channel
	433.525 MHz – U282 (SU21)
	433.550 MHz – U284 (SU22)
	433.575 MHz – U286 (SU23)
	433.600 MHz – U288 (SU24) RTTY AFSK
	433.625–433.675 MHz – packet radio
	433.700–433.775 MHz – emergency communications priority
434.600–435.000	FM repeater inputs
435.000–438.000	Satellite service and FSTV
438.000–439.800	FSTV
438.900–440.00	Packet radio

23 centimetre band

A wide range of scanners, even the tiniest handheld types, now give coverage up to 1300 MHz. This allows reception of the sections of the

Table 6.19 Recommended UK frequency allocations in the 23 centimetre band

Frequency (MHz)	Allocation
1240.000–1243.250	All modes
	1240.150–1240.750 MHz digital communications
1243.250–1260.000	ATV
	1248.000 MHz RMT1–3 TV repeater input
	1249.000 MHz RMT1–2 TV repeater input
1260.000–1270.000	Satellite service
1270.000–1272.000	All modes
1272.000–1291.500	ATV
	1276.500 MHz RMT1–1 AM TV repeater input
	1291.000–1291.500 Repeater inputs
1291.500–1296.000	All modes
1296.000–1296.150	CW
1296.150–1296.800	SSB
	1296.200 MHz centre of narrowband activity
	1296.500 MHz – SSTV 1296.700 MHz – Fax
	1296.600 MHz – RTTY
1296.800–1297.990	Beacons
1297.000–1297.475	Repeater outputs 25 kHz spacing
	1296.000 MHz – RM0 1296.200 MHz – RM8
	1296.025 MHz – RM1 1296.225 MHz – RM9
	1296.050 MHz – RM2 1296.250 MHz – RM10
	1296.075 MHz – RM3 1296.275 MHz – RM11
	1296.100 MHz – RM4 1296.300 MHz – RM12
	1296.125 MHz – RM5 1296.325 MHz – RM13
	1296.150 MHz – RM6 1296.350 MHz – RM14
	1296.175 MHz – RM7 1296.375 MHz – RM15
1297.500–1298.000	FM simplex
	1297.500 MHz – SM20 1297.650 MHz – SM26
	1297.525 MHz – SM21 1297.675 MHz – SM27
	1297.550 MHz – SM22 1297.700 MHz – SM28
	1297.575 MHz – SM23 1297.725 MHz – SM29
	1297.600 MHz – SM24 1297.750 MHz – SM30
	1297.625 MHz – SM25
1298.000–1298.500	All modes (digital communications)
1298.500–1300.000	Packet radio
	1299.000 MHz packet radio 25 kHz bandwidth
	1299.425 MHz packet radio 150 kHz bandwidth
	1299.575 MHz packet radio 150 kHz bandwidth
	1299.725 MHz packet radio 150 kHz
1300.000–1325.000	TV repeater outputs
	1308.000 MHz RMT1–3 FM TV repeater output
	1311.500 MHz RMT1–1 AM TV repeater output
	1316.000 MHz RMT1–2 FM TV repeater output

23cm band used for FM simplex and repeater communication, as well as DX communication. The latter you will normally only hear during VHF/UHF contests, such as the annual VHF National Field Day. However 23cm repeaters are horizontally polarised, although this may change in the future. A number of amateurs use 23cm to get away from the relatively congested 2m and 70cm bands, although activity is currently very low due to the high cost of equipment. However, as this comes down in price, occupancy is likely to increase.

LAND MOBILE SERVICES

Under the banner of land mobile services is a varied range of communications users. In the following section you will find listed private mobile radio, emergency services, message handling and paging. The term land mobile applies to any radio communications that take place between either mobile-to-mobile or mobile-to-base, across land as opposed to air or marine. The mobile can either be a vehicle installation or a portable transceiver of the walkie-talkie type.

Ranges of such equipment vary enormously. In open country, ranges of 20 or 30 miles are not unusual but in built-up areas this may be cut to considerably less. Users of mobile radio equipment operating in towns and cities often use aerials on very high buildings well away from the actual point of operation. Connection between the operator and the remote aerial site is usually through a dedicated landline or a radio/microwave link. Emergency services may have even more sophisticated arrangements with several aerial/transmitter sites to give total coverage of an area. This becomes particularly important when communication is to and from low powered handsets with limited aerial facilities.

Private mobile radio (PMR)

Private mobile radio is a form of communication between a base station and one or more mobile or portable units. Typical examples are the transceivers used by taxi firms. PMR is not to be confused with the government allocations, emergency services or cellphones, all of which fall into different categories and are listed elsewhere.

Communication in the PMR bands can be either FM or AM and may be split frequency, or single frequency simplex. Only one band, VHF band III is available for duplex working. Table 6.20 shows some of the bands allocated to PMR communications in the UK, listing them with respect to frequency and service allocations.

Cellphones

The cellular telephone system relies on a whole network of base stations. The cellphone system is computer-controlled and as the cellphone itself moves out of range of one base station it is automatically switched to the

Table 6.20 UK private mobile radio bands and frequency allocations

Frequency (MHz)	Allocation
55.7500–60.7500	Experimental UK low-band PMR
62.7500–68.0000	Experimental UK low-band PMR
68.08125–70.00625	Base/simplex Tx
71.50625–72.79375	Mobile Tx
76.70625–77.99375	Mobile Tx
81.50625–83.50000	Base Tx
85.00625–87.49375	Base Tx/simplex
139.5125–140.4875	Fuel and power industries
148.0125–148.9875	Fuel and power industries
158.53125–160.54375	Base Tx
163.03125–168.24375	Mobile Tx
168.24375–168.30625	Simplex PMR
168.84375–169.39375	Simplex PMR
169.81875–173.09375	Mobile Tx/simplex PMR
177.20625–181.69375	Base Tx PAMR/PMR
181.80625–183.49375	Base Tx PAMR/PMR
185.20625–189.69375	Mobile Tx PAMR/PMR
189.80625–191.49375	Mobile Tx PAMR/PMR
193.20625–199.49375	Mobile Tx PAMR/PMR
201.20625–207.49375	Base Tx PAMR/PMR
209.20625–210.20625	Base Tx PAMR/PMR
212.55625–213.55625	Mobile Tx PAMR/PMR
210.91875–211.91875	Base Tx narrowband
214.26875–215.26875	Mobile Tx narrowband
410.0000–415.0000	Mobile Tx TETRA PMR
420.0000–425.0000	Base Tx TETRA PMR
425.00625–427.75625	Mobile Tx
428.01875–428.99375	Mobile Tx
431.00000–432.00000	Mobile Tx London only
440.00625–442.25625	Base Tx
442.51875–443.49375	Base Tx
445.50625–446.40625	Base Tx
447.51875–449.49375	Base Tx London only
453.00625–453.99375	Mobile Tx
454.8375–454.9875	Simplex
455.46875–455.85625	Airports only
455.99375–456.99375	Mobile Tx
459.51875–460.49375	Base Tx
460.76875–461.23125	Airports only
461.25625–462.49375	Mobile Tx and simplex

frequency of the next closest cell. Inter-site links commonly use microwave dishes, and portable to portable calls as well as to and from the PSTN (Public Switched Telephone Network) are used.

Short Range Business Radio (SRBR) and PMR446

These are services designed for use with 500m watt handhelds only for short-range and on-site use. SRBR was introduced to the UK as an interim measure for business communication only, and will be phased out by 2003. PMR446 operates on 8 channels, is an EU-harmonised allocation and may be used for any purpose. CTCSS or DCS is used on these services.

Table 6.21 SRBR and PMR446 allocated frequencies

SRBR	461.2625 MHz	PMR446	446.00625 MHz
	461.4750 MHz		446.01875 MHz
	461.4875 MHz		446.03125 MHz
			446.04375 MHz
			446.05625 MHz
			446.06875 MHz
			446.08125 MHz
			446.09375 MHz

Wide area paging

This service provides for one-way transmissions from a base station to a small pocket receiver. The transmission is coded to activate only the required pager, and the most common system used is POCSAG, although the FLEX proprietary protocol is also used, ERMES is a pan-European paging system. The simplest form of pagers merely emit a bleeping sound to alert the holder that they are wanted. Some of the more sophisticated types can receive a short alphanumeric message that appears on a small liquid crystal display. Wide area pagers usually cover a specific area such as a town but a number of services also cover most of the country. Wide area paging should not be confused with on-site paging. Table 6.22 lists wide area paging allocated frequencies

Table 6.22 Wide area paging allocated frequencies

VHF	137.9625–138.2125 MHz	UHF	454.0125–454.8375 MHz
	153.0125–153.4875 MHz		466.0625–466·0875 MHz
	169.4125–169.8125 MHz (ERMES)		

On-site paging

Similar to wide area paging but low powered and operating over a small area such as a factory, building site, etc. Sometimes the pager has a small and simple transmitter which allows the user to acknowledge that the paging signal has been received. AM or FM modes may be transmitted, and data communications are possible. Table 6.23 lists on-site paging allocated frequencies and services. At VHF a 12.5 kHz channel spacing is used, at UHF 25 kHz.

Table 6.23 On-site paging allocated frequencies

VHF band	Allocation
31.7125–31.7875 MHz	Hospital paging
47.400 MHz	Vehicle paging alarms
48.9750–49.49375 MHz	On-site paging
	49.4250 MHz – hospitals
	49.4375 MHz – hospitals
	49.4500 MHz – hospitals
	49.4625 MHz – hospitals
	49.4750 MHz – hospitals
160.99375–161.20625 MHz	On-site, with return speech acknowledgment allowed for hospital in emergencies
UHF band	**Allocation**
458.8375–459.4875 MHz	On-site
	458.900 MHz – vehicle paging and some car radio keyfobs

Land emergency services

Land emergency services are normally police, fire and ambulance services. Some services are also found on bands allocated to PMR but nearly all police forces operate in bands allocated to the UK Home Office. In addition to the bands listed in Table 6.24, emergency services in some areas may be located in government mobile allocations (see Table 6.1).

Table 6.24 Land emergency services band and allocated frequencies

Frequency (MHz)	Allocation
Band: VHF low (12.5 kHz channel spacing, AM)	
70.5000-71.5000	Fire bases
81.9000–83.9000	Fire mobiles
80.00–84.00	Mobile Tx
97.60–102.10	Base Tx
Band: VHF high (12.5 kHz channel spacing, AM/FM)	
143.00–144.0000	Mobile Tx
152.00–153.0000	Base Tx
147.2000–148.0000	Mobile Tx
155.2000–156.0000	Base Tx
146.0000–147.2000	Fixed links
166.2750–166.5250	Ambulances
Band: UHF low (12.5 kHz channel spacing, FM)	
420.00–425.00	
429.00–432.00	
443.50–445.00	
446.00–450.00	
451.000–453.000	
459.50–470.00	
464.9000–467.0000	

Comment: Usually split frequency simplex but channel pairings vary.

Table 6.25 Ambulance services

Area	Base	Mobile	Call	Channel
Avon	166.5000	171.3000		117
Bedfordshire	166.3375	171.1375		104
Bedfordshire	166.4625	171.2625		114
Bedfordshire	166.7750	171.5750		139
Berkshire	166.3875	171.1875		108
Berkshire	166.6125	171.4125		126
Buckinghamshire	166.2875	171.0870		100
Buckinghamshire	166.5625	171.3625		122
Cambridgeshire	166.3125	171.1125		102
Cambridgeshire	166.3500	171.1500		105
Cheshire	166.3625	171.1625		106
Cleveland	166.2000	171.0000		93
Cleveland	166.3500	171.1500		105
Clwyd	166.4125	171.2125		110
Clwyd	166.4625	171.2625		114
Clwyd	166.5625	171.3625		122
Cornwall	166.2875	171.0870		100

Area	Base	Mobile	Call	Channel
Cornwall	166.5000	171.3000		117
County Durham	166.5875	171.3875		124
Cumbria	166.3000	171.1000		101
Cumbria	166.3500	171.1500		105
Cumbria	166.3750	171.1750		107
Derby	166.2875	171.0870		100
Derby	166.3125	171.1125		102
Derbyshire	166.3750	171.1750		107
Devon	166.3125	171.1125		102
Devon	166.5625	171.3625		122
Doctors common	166.8125	171.6125		1
Dorset	166.2000	171.0000		93
Dorset	166.3000	171.1000		101
Dorset	166.4875	171.2875		116
Dorset	166.5250	171.3250		119
Dorset	166.8375	171.6375		144
East Anglia	166.0500	170.8500		
East Anglia	166.3500	171.1500		105
East Anglia	166.3625	171.1625		106
East Anglia	166.4375	171.2375		112
East Anglia	166.5250	171.3250		119
Essex	166.3625	171.1625		106
Essex	166.4875	171.2875		116
Essex	166.5500	171.3500		121
Glamorgan	166.7750	171.5750		139
Glamorgan (mid)	166.3250	171.1250		103
Glamorgan (mid)	166.5250	171.3250		119
Glamorgan (S)	166.3000	171.1000		101
Glamorgan (S)	166.4750	171.2750		115
Glamorgan (S)	166.5875	171.3875		124
Glamorgan (W)	166.3500	171.1500		105
Glamorgan (W)	166.8250	171.6250		143
Gloucestershire	166.3625	171.1625		106
Gloucestershire	166.8000	171.6000		142
Gloucestershire	166.8375	171.6375		144
Guernsey	86.4250			
Gwent	166.4000	171.2000		109
Gwent	166.5750	171.3750		123
Gwynedd	166.4750	171.2750		115
Hampshire	166.3625	171.1625		106
Hampshire	166.5750	171.3750		123
Hampshire	166.5875	171.3875		124
Hampshire	166.7750	171.5750		139
Hatfield	166.6125	171.4125		2
Hatfield	166.8125	171.6125		1
Herefordshire	166.3750	171.1750		107
Herefordshire	166.4750	171.2750		115
Herefordshire	166.5625	171.3625		122
Herefordshire	166.6125	171.4125		126

Area	Base	Mobile	Call	Channel
Herefordshire	166.8250	171.6250		143
Hertfordshire	166.5875	171.3875		124
Humberside	166.3000	171.1000		101
Humberside	166.3250	171.1250		103
Humberside	166.4000	171.2000		109
Humberside	166.5250	171.3250		119
Humberside	166.5750	171.3750		123
Humberside	166.6125	171.4125		126
Isle of Wight	166.3375	171.1375		104
Isles of Scilly	166.5000	171.3000		117
Jersey	154.6625	146.1125	Jersam	1
Jersey	154.7500	146.2250	Jersam	2
Kent	166.2875	171.0875		100
Kent	166.3375	171.1375		104
Kent	166.3875	171.1875		108
Kent	166.8250	171.6250		143
Lancashire	166.2750	171.0750		99
Lancashire	166.3875	171.1875		108
Lancashire	166.5500	171.3500		121
Leicestershire	166.4125	171.2125		110
Leicestershire	166.5375	171.3375		120
Leicestershire	166.3000	171.1000		101
Lincolnshire	166.2000	171.0000		93
Lincolnshire	166.2750	171.0750		99
Lincolnshire	166.3625	171.1625		106
Lincolnshire	166.4000	171.2000		109
London	165.6250	170.4250		3
London	165.6375	170.4750		2
London	165.6500	170.8500		1
London	166.1000	170.9000		6
London	166.1250	170.9250	Red	5
London	166.3125	171.1125	Red	1
London	166.4375	171.2375	Red	15
London	166.5250	171.3250	Red	4
London	166.5750	171.3750	White	10
London (E)	166.3500	171.1500	Red	2
London (NE)	166.3000	171.1000	Gold	9
London (NE)	166.4250	171.2250	Gold	7
London (NE)	166.5000	171.3000	Gold	8
London (NW)	166.4500	171.2500	Blue	6
London (NW)	166.4750	171.2750	Blue	5
London (S)	166.4125	171.2125	Red	3
London (SE)	166.2000	171.0000	Green	13
London (SE)	166.3250	171.1250	Orange	12
London (SE)	166.3750	171.1750	Green	14
London (SW)	166.2750	171.0750	Orange	11
Manchester	166.2875	171.0870		100
Manchester	166.3000	171.1000		101
Manchester	166.4875	171.2875		116

121

Area	Base	Mobile	Call	Channel
Manchester	166.5000	171.3000		117
Manchester	166.5125	171.3125		118
Manchester	166.6000	171.4000		125
Merseyside	166.3250	171.1250		103
Merseyside	166.3375	171.1375		104
Merseyside	166.4750	171.2750		115
Merseyside	166.5875	171.3875		124
Midlands (W)	166.2750	171.0750		99
Midlands (W)	166.3500	171.1500		105
Midlands (W)	166.4625	171.2625		114
Midlands (W)	166.5500	171.3500		121
Midlands (W)	166.6000	171.4000		125
National	87.6500	77.6500		
National	166.1000	170.9000		
National	166.6000	171.4000		
National	166.6125	171.4125		
Norfolk	166.4375	171.2375		1
Norfolk	166.5625	171.3625		2
Northern Ireland	87.5500	77.5500		
Northern Ireland	87.5750	77.5750		
Northern Ireland	87.6250	77.6250		
Northern Ireland	87.6500	77.6500		
Northern Ireland	87.6750	77.6750		
Northern Ireland	87.5250	77.5250		
Northumbria	166.2875	171.0870		100
Northumbria	166.4000	171.2000		109
Northumbria	166.4875	171.2875		116
Northumbria	166.5125	171.3125		118
Northumbria	166.5750	171.3750		123
Northumbria	166.6000	171.4000		125
Northamptonshire	166.5500	171.3500		121
Northamptonshire	166.5750	171.3750		123
Nottinghamshire	166.4125	171.2125		110
Oxfordshire	166.4875	171.2875		116
Oxfordshire	166.6125	171.4125		126
Pembrokeshire	166.3625	171.1625		106
Powys	166.2875	171.0870		100
Powys	166.3125	171.1125		102
Private national	72.5375			
Private national	86.0375			
Red Cross	86.3250			
Red Cross	86.4125			
Somerset	166.2750	171.0750		99
Somerset	166.3375	171.1375		104
St John	86.3250			
St John	86.4125			
St John	169.3625			
Staffordshire	166.3875	171.1875		108
Staffordshire	166.5000	171.3000		117

Area	Base	Mobile	Call	Channel
Staffordshire	166.5875	171.3875		124
Staffordshire	166.6125	171.4125		126
Staffordshire	166.7500	171.7500		137
Suffolk	166.5250	171.3250		119
Suffolk	166.3500	171.1500		105
Suffolk (W)	166.3375	171.1375		104
Surrey	166.2875	171.0870		100
Surrey	166.5125	171.3125		118
Surrey	166.5375	171.3375		120
Surrey	166.7500	171.7500		137
Sussex (E)	166.4000	171.2000		109
Sussex (W)	166.4625	171.2625		114
Sussex (W)	166.5625	171.3625		122
Welwyn	166.6125	171.4125		2
Welwyn	166.8125	171.6125		1
Wiltshire	166.4125	171.2125		110
Wiltshire	166.6125	171.4125		126
Worcestershire	166.3750	171.1750		107
Worcestershire	166.4750	171.2750		115
Worcestershire	166.5625	171.3625		122
Worcestershire	166.8250	171.6250		143
Yorkshire	166.2000	171.0000		93
Yorkshire	166.3875	171.1875		108
Yorkshire (N)	166.3375	171.1375		104
Yorkshire (N)	166.4625	171.2625		114
Yorkshire (N)	166.4750	171.2750		115
Yorkshire (N)	166.5000	171.3000		117
Yorkshire (N)	166.5250	171.3250		119
Yorkshire (N)	166.5375	171.3375		120
Yorkshire (N)	166.6125	171.4125		126
Yorkshire (S)	166.4000	171.2000		109
Yorkshire (S)	166.4875	171.2875		116
Yorkshire (S)	166.5500	171.3500		121
Yorkshire (S)	166.5625	171.3625		122
Yorkshire (W)	166.3000	171.1000		101
Yorkshire (W	166.4000	171.2000		109
Yorkshire (W)	166.4125	171.2125		110
Yorkshire (W)	166.4625	171.2625		114
Yorkshire (W)	166.5375	171.3375		120

UHF allocations for Regional Health Authorities

457.400	2	Yorkshire
457.4250	2	Yorkshire
	4	East Anglia
457.4500	1	Northern
457.4750	4	East Anglia
457.5000	4	East Anglia
457.5250	12	West Midlands

UHF allocations for Regional Health Authorities

457.5750		12	West Midlands
457.6250			Wales
457.6750	166.335	4	East Anglia
457.7250		1	Northern
457.7500			Wales
457.7750		4	East Anglia
457.9750		4	East Anglia
458.0000		2	Yorkshire
458.0250		5 6 7 8	Thames
458.0500		3	Trent
		11	South West
458.1250		1	Northern
458.1500		12	West Midlands
458.1750		2	Yorkshire
		12	West Midlands
			Wales
458.2250		4	East Anglia
			Wales
458.2500		2	Yorkshire
458.3000			Wales
458.3250		1	Northern
		5 6 7 8	Thames
458.3500		1	Northern
458.4250		5 6 7 8	Thames
458.4750			Wales
459.7750			Jersey
460.5750		5 6 7 8	Thames
		11	South West
460.6000		10	Oxford
460.6250		1	Northern
		10	Oxford
460.6500			Wales
460.675		1	Northern
		2	Yorkshire
460.725		11	South West
460.750		1	Northern
461.275		1	Northern
		2	Yorkshire
		5 6 7 8	Thames
		12	West Midlands
			Wales
461.300		2	Yorkshire
		5 6 7 8	Thames
		10	Oxford
			Wales
461.325		10	Oxford
461.350		10	Oxford
			Wales
461.375		10	Oxford

UHF allocations for Regional Health Authorities

Frequency	Code	Region
461.475	10	Oxford
		Wales
462.925	4	East Anglia
462.950	1	Northern
	9	Wessex
		Wales
462.975	4	East Anglia
463.000 166.525	4	East Anglia
463.050	10	Oxford
463.075	4	East Anglia
463.100	1	Northern
		Wales
463.150	1	Northern
		Wales
463.175 166.3375	4	East Anglia
463.225		Wales
463.250	4	East Anglia
463.500	9	Wessex
463.525	1	Northern
	4	East Anglia
463.550		Wales
463.600	9	Wessex
		Wales
463.625	1	Northern
	9	Wessex
	12	West Midlands
463.650	5 6 7 8	Thames
463.700	12	West Midlands
463.750	9	Wessex
	12	West Midlands
463.825	1	Northern
		Wales
463.850	1	Northern
		Wales
463.900	5 6 7 8	Thames
463.925	1	Northern
		Wales
463.950	5 6 7 8	Thames
	9	Wessex
	12	West Midlands
463.975	12	West Midlands
467.025	12	West Midlands
467.050		Wales
467.125	1	Northern
467.175	1	Northern
467.225	11	South West
467.250	1	Northern Wales
467.475		Wales
467.775		Wales

UHF allocations for Regional Health Authorities

467.800	Wales
467.825	Wales
467.900	Wales
467.925	Wales

1	Northern:	Cleveland, Cumbria, Durham, Northumbria
2	Yorkshire:	Yorkshire, Humberside
3	Trent:	Derbyshire, Leicestershire, Lincolnshire, Nottinghamshire, S. Yorkshire
4	East Anglia:	Cambridgeshire, Norfolk, E. Suffolk
5	NW Thames:	N. Bedfordshire, E. Hertfordshire
6	NE Thames:	Mid Essex
7	SE Thames:	Eastbourne, Medway, Kent
8	SW Thames:	Mid Surrey, W. Sussex
9	Wessex:	E. Dorset, Hampshire, Isle of Wight
10	Oxford:	W. Berkshire, Buckinghamshire, Northamptonshire, Oxford
11	South West:	Avon, Cornwall, Devon, Gloucester, Scilly Isles, Somerset
12	West Midlands:	Hereford, Mid Staffordshire, Salop, South Warwickshire, Worcestershire
13	Mersey:	Cheshire, Merseyside

Table 6.26 Fire Brigades VHF

Band	Allocation

Band: VHF High (12.5 kHz channel spacing (AM/FM)

70.5125–71.5000	Fire bases
80.0000–82.5000	Fire mobiles
146.0000–148.000	Fire mobiles
154.0000–156.000	Fire bases

Area	Base	Mobile	Call	Channel
Avon & Somerset	71.0125	80.1750	M2QG	
Avon & Somerset	154.5000		M2QC	
Bedfordshire	71.1125		M2VM	
Berkshire	154.0750	146.1750	M2HD	
Berkshire	71.2000		M2HD	
Buckinghamshire	71.1375	80.1125	M2HK	
Cambridgeshire	154.1250	146.1750	M2VP	
Cambridgeshire	70.8375		M2VC	
Cambridgeshire	71.4250		M2VC	
Cheshire	154.2250		M2CF	
Cheshire	154.6500		M2CF	
Cheshire	155.5750	146.2875	M2CF	
Cheshire	70.7750	80.5000	M2CF	
Cleveland	71.1125		M2LT	
Clwyd	71.1625	80.8750	M2WK	
Cornwall	70.7875	80.8000	M2QA	
County Durham	70.8875	80.2125	M2LF	
Cumbria	70.8375	80.0375	M2BC	

Area	Base	Mobile	Call	Channel
Derbyshire	154.0500	146.5375	M2ND	
Derbyshire	70.7125	80.8000	M2ND	
Devon	70.7250	80.0375	M2QD	
Devon	70.8250	80.0375	M2QD	
Devon & Cornwall	154.0750	146.1750	M2QA	
Dorset	70.8625	80.5500	M2QK	
Dyfed	70.6125	80.1250	M2WV	
East Anglia	154.6500	146.1125		
East London	70.7625	80.1500	M2FE	3
Essex	70.6250	80.6125	M2VD	1
Essex	70.7250	80.6750	M2VD	2
Essex	70.9125		M2VD	
Gloucestershire	71.0750	80.6250	M2QF	
Gloucestershire	71.3875		M2QC	
Gloucestershire	154.3125		M2QF	2
Greater Manchester	70.5875	80.7625	M2FT	3
Greater Manchester	70.5250	80.7375	M2FT	2
Greater Manchester	70.5500		M2FT	
Greater Manchester	70.8250	80.7875	M2FT	4
Gwent	70.7000	81.1250	M2WP	
Gwynedd	70.8125	81.2125	M2WC	
Hampshire	154.5750		M2HX	
Hampshire	154.7625		M2HX	
Hampshire	155.3375		M2HX	
Hampshire	70.5875	80.1875	M2HX	2
Hampshire	70.7750	80.5000	M2HX	1
Hampshire (N)	154.8750		M2ND	
Handsets	154.6875			
Hereford & Worcester	70.6875	81.1250	M2YB	
Hereford & Worcester	154.3000		M2YB	
Hereford & Worcester	155.4000		M2YB	
Hertfordshire	70.9000	80.0375	M2VI	
Humberside	154.6000		M2XT	
Humberside	154.8250	146.7000	M2XT	
Humberside	71.0750		M2XT	
Humberside	71.1000	80.6625	M2XT	
Humberside (N)	154.7750		XT	
Isle of Wight	71.2750	81.0625	M2HP	
Kent	154.4750	146.1750	M2HO5	
Kent	154.7500		M2KA1	
Kent	70.8375	80.0375	M2KF	
Lancashire	70.5250	80.9625	M2MP	2
Lancashire	71.3875		M2BE	3
Lancashire	70.6750	80.5500	M2BE	1
Lancashire	70.9000	80.6000	M2BE	4
Leamington	155.2250		M2YS	
Leicestershire	70.6625	81.0000	M2NK	
Lincolnshire	70.5625	80.6000	M2NV	
London	154.1250	146.1750	M2FN	

127

Area	Base	Mobile	Call	Channel
London	154.1750	146.3500	M2FS2	
London	154.6750	146.2750	M2FE3	
London	154.8250	147.6125	M2FN4	
London	71.3000		M2FH 5	
London (N)	71.1750	80.2125	M2FN	4
London (S)	70.9626	80.1125	M2FS	2
London Central	70.5250	80.9625	M2FH	1
Merseyside	70.6250		M2FO	3
Merseyside	70.7000		M2FO	4
Merseyside	70.9625	81.0875	M2FO	2
Merseyside	71.0375	81.0625	M2FO	
Mid Glamorgan	70.5625	80.6000	M2WF	
Norfolk	70.7000		M2VF	
Norfolk	154.4000		M2VF	
Norfolk	154.7250		M2VF	
Norfolk	154.8500		M2VF	
North Yorkshire	71.1375	80.4375	M2LY	
North Yorkshire	71.1750		M2LY	
Northamptonshire	70.7500	80.7500	M2N0	
Northumberland	70.5125	80.1875	M2LJ	
Nottinghamshire	154.6750	146.2750	M2NZ	
Nottinghamshire	70.5375	80.1875	M2NZ	
Oxfordshire	71.1000	80.6625	M2HI	
Powys	70.8500	80.9625	M2WB	
Shropshire	70.9750	80.6500	M2YU	
Somerset	71.1250	80.1125	M2QI	
South Glamorgan	70.6750	80.5250	M2WD	
South Yorkshire	70.6375	80.2125	M2XY	
Staffordshire	154.1250	146.1750	M2YG	
Staffordshire	154.2250	146.7000	M2YG	
Staffordshire	154.4750	146.1750	M2YG	
Staffordshire	155.6000		M2YG	
Staffordshire	70.8875	80.9375	M2YG	
Suffolk	71.2750	81.0875	M2VN	
Surrey	70.6125	80.1250	M2HF	
Surrey	146.0250		M2HF	
Sussex	70.6375	80.2125	M2KD	
Sussex (E)	154.8250	146.6125	M2KW	
Sussex (W)	70.8000	80.5125	M2KW	
Sussex (W)	154.8000	146.7250	M2KW	
Thames Valley	154.0750	146.1750	M2HI	
Thames Valley	154.5500		M2HI	
Tyne and Wear	71.3000		M2LP	
Tyne and Wear	71.3000		M2LP	2
Wales	154.8750	146.0375	M2WP	
Wales	154.9500	146.0125	M2WP	
Warwickshire	70.6000	80.2625	M2YS	
West Glamorgan	70.9500		M2WZ	
West Midlands	70.5125	80.4375	M2BW	1

Area	Base	Mobile	Call	Channel
West Midlands	154.2500		M2FB	
West Midlands	155.4500		M2FB	
West Midlands	70.5750	80.4625	M2F0	3
West Midlands	71.1500	80.5125	M2EW	2
West Yorkshire	70.7625		M2XF	
West Yorkshire	70.6125		M2XF	
West Yorkshire	70.8750		M2XF	
Wiltshire	154.1250	146.1750	M2QM	
Wiltshire	154.4750	146.1750	M2QM	
Wiltshire	70.6500	80.9875	M2QM	
Yorkshire	154.0500	146.5375	M2XK	

Table 6.27 Police UHF allocations

Frequency (MHz)	Allocation
Band: UHF (25 kHz channel spacing, FM)	
450.0000–453.0000	Base transmit
464.0000–466.9000	Mobile transmit

Citizens' Band (CB) radio

Citizens' Band radio communications originated in the USA where it was felt there was a need for a low powered, short distance communication system. The idea was for a low-cost service with the minimum of regulations where the user did not have to comply with strict licensing conditions to prove an essential use for two-way radio. It was to give such people as small businesses, servicemen, truckers, farmers and social organisations a means of communications.

The UK started off with an illegal CB service using the same channel allocations as those in the USA – AM equipment, designed for America, was smuggled into Britain. CB became such a craze that thousands of illegal transceivers were in use and often caused havoc to legitimate users of the frequencies which included radio modellers, paging systems and meteorological equipment. Finally, the government, which appeared reluctant to establish a legal service, gave in. The service introduced in November 1981 had slightly different frequencies to the American equipment and used frequency modulation. Britain now has two CB allocations at 27 MHz (see Table 6.28), the CEPT band being harmonised across Europe and which uses the same channels as the US allocation. Even so, unapproved American equipment and power amplifiers, illegal in the EU, are used from time to time, particularly when conditions favour long distance contact.

Range

Across open country usable HF ranges of up to 20 or more miles can be expected but a lot will depend on circumstances, i.e., base-base, base-mobile or mobile-mobile working. Ranges are considerably reduced in built-up areas but under lift conditions ranges may become almost global. The band is very prone to the effects of the 11-year sunspot cycle and when that happens it is not unusual to hear transmissions from the USA, Australia, Asia, South America, etc. Note that ranges quoted are only likely to be achieved by using a proper CB aerial. Most discone-type aerials, favoured for scanner operation, operate quite poorly at lower frequencies.

Table 6.28 UK and European CB channels

Channel	Frequencies (MHz) UK	CEPT	Channel	Frequencies (MHz) UK	CEPT
01	27.60125	26.965	21	27.80125	27.215
02	27.61125	26.975	22	27.81125	27.225
03	27.62125	26.985	23	27.82125	27.255
04	27.63125	27.005	24	27.83125	27.235
05	27.64125	27.015	25	27.84125	27.245
06	27.65125	27.025	26	27.85125	27.265
07	27.66125	27.035	27	27.86125	27.275
08	27.67125	27.055	28	27.87125	27.285
09	27.68125	27.065	29	27.88125	27.295
10	27.69125	27.075	30	27.89125	27.305
11	27.70125	27.085	31	27.90125	27.315
12	27.71125	27.105	32	27.91125	27.325
13	27.72125	27.115	33	27.92125	27.335
14	27.73125	27.125	34	27.93125	27.345
15	27.74125	27.135	35	27.94125	27.355
16	27.75125	27.155	36	27.95125	27.365
17	27.76125	27.165	37	27.96125	27.375
18	27.77125	27.175	38	27.97125	27.385
19	27.78125	27.185	39	27.98125	27.395
20	27.79125	27.205	40	27.99125	27.405

7 ▉ RT (Radio Telephony) procedure

English is the most internationally accepted language in radio communications, yet many communicators appear to have a language all of their own. There's a good reason for some of the codes, abbreviations and expressions that are used on the air: so that misunderstandings can be avoided. The use of a set of common expressions means that even people who speak different languages can send and receive basic messages correctly. In some cases, however (early CB being a good example), the expressions used are just part of the tradition which goes with the medium. We shall first consider some things that are common to most operators.

PHONETIC ALPHABET

Sometimes, under difficult conditions, it may be impossible to tell what the user transmitting from another station is saying. Under such circumstances it is usual to spell out the message, coding the letters as words, using the phonetic alphabet:

A	Alpha	J	Juliet	S	Sierra
B	Bravo	K	Kilo	T	Tango
C	Charlie	L	Lima	U	Uniform
D	Delta	M	Mike	V	Victor
E	Echo	N	November	W	Whisky
F	Foxtrot	O	Oscar	X	X-ray
G	Golf	P	Papa	Y	Yankee
H	Hotel	Q	Quebec	Z	Zulu
I	India	R	Roger		

These phonetics are widely used in callsigns. For instance, amateur station G4XYZ would be Golf Four X-Ray Yankee Zulu. Similar use of phonetics will be heard in aircraft callsigns which are usually made up of a string of letters with the first or first two letters, denoting the country of registration. Some expressions are common to most radio users:

Roger	An almost universal expression meaning 'I understand or acknowledge receipt of your message.
Wilco	Not very common nowadays – mainly heard in early cinema films rather than on the air currently. It means 'I will comply with your instructions'.
Copy	A message or part of it. For instance, the expression 'I copy you' means 'I am able to understand you, I hear you'.
Mayday	The international call of distress where grave and imminent danger is present. The word is repeated three times and means that an emergency situation has occurred. All stations on the frequency, except that calling *Mayday* and that providing assistance, should observe strict radio silence.
Pan-Pan	A call indicating that assistance is required urgently but no-one is in immediate danger. This may be followed some time later by a Mayday if the situation deteriorates.
Securité	A call giving safety and navigational information, typically of potential hazards.
Affirmative	Yes.
Negative	No.

TIME

Even within the relatively close confines of Europe many countries may be in different time zones and so a standard time system has been adopted so that complex calculations can be avoided during radio communications. Coordinated Universal Time (UTC) is the same time as Greenwich Mean Time (GMT). Occasionally, some radio operators will refer to UTC as Zulu, e.g., '1500 hours Zulu' is 3 o'clock in the afternoon. British summer time (BST) is known as Alpha, that is, UTC + 1 hour. Virtually all radio traffic references to time are made using the 24-hour clock system.

AMATEURS

Amateurs form one of only two groups of radio users (the other is CB) who usually transmit blind: that is they put out calls for contact with anyone who happens to be on the same frequency or channel. Professional users, on the other hand, except in emergencies, only put out calls for specific stations. But amateurs, too, might well call up particular stations and, even when transmitting blind, they may well specify that they only want contacts into a certain area. For instance, it is not unusual under lift conditions to hear UK amateurs calling for contacts on the continent or even from a specific country. While most amateurs will happily chat to anyone who happens to be on the air many will, at times, only want to work long distances. One of the attractions of the hobby is being able, on occasions, to work not only far-flung places but also small countries where there may only be a few amateurs. Such 'catches' are a little bit like a stamp collector finding a rare stamp. Amateurs use expressions known as Q-codes to abbreviate messages (some typical Q-codes follow). Note that most can be either a statement or a question, e.g., QRP can mean 'shall I reduce my power?' or 'reduce your power', depending on the context of use.

INTERNATIONAL Q-CODES

QRM Interference. This is man-made, such as noise from electrical equipment.

QRN Interference. Natural interference, such as static.

QRP Reducing transmitter power. The expression QRP station means a transmitter that is always operated at very low power. Some amateurs specialise in this kind of operation.

QRT Stop sending/transmitting. A station saying 'I am going QRT' usually means he is closing down.

QRZ Who is calling?

QSB Signals fading.

QSK 'Can I break in on your contact?'. Often a query from a station wanting to join in a net, i.e. a group of amateurs passing conversation back and forth.

QSL Acknowledge receipt. A QSL card is an acknowledgement card sent to confirm a contact and is often collected in order to claim awards.

QSO Communicate or communication. For example 'I had a QSO with a French station'.

QSY Change frequency or channel. For example 'Let's QSY to 144.310 MHz'.

QTH Location of station. Sometimes you may hear the expression 'QTH locator'. This is a grid system used by amateurs to work out the distances between each other.

There are many other Q-codes but they are rarely used by amateurs using speech for communications.

Reporting codes

Amateurs, like other radio users, have a system of reporting on the signal that they receive. The other station will usually find this information useful as it can tell him what propagation conditions are like and if his equipment is performing correctly. Like some scanners, amateur radio transceivers usually have a signal strength meter to indicate received signal strength. The lower part of the scale is usually marked from 0 to 9, above this the scale is marked in decibels (dB). The internationally recognised method of reporting on signals is known as the RST code: R is readability, S is signal strength and T is tone. For speech communication the T is not used as it applies only to Morse code. Amateurs will usually be heard to say something like 'you are five and nine' meaning readability 5, signal strength 9. The code follows:

Readability
- R1   Unreadable
- R2   Barely readable
- R3   Readable with considerable difficulty
- R4   Readable with practically no difficulty
- R5   Perfectly readable

Signal strength
- S1   Faint, barely perceptible
- S2   Very weak
- S3   Weak
- S4   Fair
- S5   Fairly good
- S6   Good
- S7   Moderately strong
- S8   Strong
- S9   Extremely strong
- S9+ Meter needle exceeding S9 level of the scale

The last one is an unofficial code but is often used and a corresponding measurement may be given in decibels, e.g., 'You are 20dB over 9'.

Callsign prefixes

It's possible to identify the country from which a station is transmitting by the first few letters and/or numbers of the callsign. Table 7.1 lists typical countries whose stations may be heard in the UK on VHF and UHF under some lift conditions.

Table 7.1 Amateur callsign prefixes, with associated countries

Prefix	Country	Prefix	Country	Prefix	Country
C3	Andorra	GW, GC, MW	Wales	PA, PB, PD, PE, PI	Netherlands
CN	Morocco	HA, HG	Hungary		
CT1CQ-CT2, 4-8,0	Portugal	HB	Switzerland	SM, SH-SL	Sweden
		HB0	Lichtenstein	SV, SX-SZ	Greece
DL, DA-DD, DF-DH, DJ, DK, DP	Germany	HV	Vatican City	SV9	Crete
		I	Italy	TA	Turkey
EA, EB-EH1-5, 7, 0	Spain	LA, LB, LC, LG, LI, LJ, LN	Norway	TF	Iceland
				T9	Bosnia-Herzegovina
EA6, EB6-EH6	Balearic Isles	LX	Luxembourg	UA, U, UE 1,3, 4,6	European Russia
EA8, EB8-EH8	Canary Isles	LZ	Bulgaria		
EA9, EB9-EH9	Ceuta/Mellila	OE	Austria	UR US-UZ	Ukraine
EI, EJ	Eire	OH, OF, OG, OI	Finland	YO, YP-YR	Rumania
EL	Liberia	OH0, OF0, OG0	Aaland Island	ZB, ZG	Gibraltar
F	France	OJ0, OF0M, OH0M	Market Reef	3A	Monaco
G, GX, M	England			3V	Tunisia
GD, GT, MD	Isle of Man	OK, OL	Czech Republic	4N1,6-0	Yugoslavia YU
GI, GN, MI N.	Ireland	ON, OO-OT	Belgium	4U1	United Nations
GJ, GH, MJ	Jersey (CI)	OT	Greenland	7X, 7W	Algeria
GM, GS, MM	Scotland	OX	Faroe Island	9A	Croatia
GU, MU	Guernsey (CI)	OZ	Denmark	9H	Malta

Contest stations

Occasionally you may hear contests in operation. Participating stations, operated by an individual or a group, are required to make as many contacts as possible within a given space of time. A major UK-based VHF/UHF contest which you may hear on your scanner is probably the VHF National Field Day (VHF NFD) which is organised by the Radio Society of Great Britain. This takes place every year on the first weekend in July between 3.00pm on the Saturday and 3.00pm on the Sunday. During the event the whole spectrum around plus and minus a few hundred kilohertz of 144.300 MHz (2m) and 432.200 MHz (70cm) comes alive with thousands of transmitting stations. Most of the transmissions are SSB utilising Upper Sideband, so will only be of interest to owners of suitably equipped scanners. However, for such owners this event usually provides an occasion to hear a lot of long distance stations. Lift conditions are normally good at this time of year and many continental stations beam their transmission towards the UK in order to take part in the contest.

Special event stations

Occasionally you may hear special event stations which are usually operated by a group of amateurs such as an amateur radio club. They are granted a special one-off callsign to celebrate special events such as a country fair or a scout Jamboree-on-the-air. Callsigns are often granted to have some significance to the event. For instance, amateurs operating from the Totnes Agricultural Fair might use the callsign GB2TAF. The GB prefix is the normal one used for special event stations although many stations use the GX prefix to allow transmissions of a short greetings message by visitors to the station.

Repeaters

Details of how repeaters work were outlined in Chapter 2. Repeaters in the 6 metre, 2 metre, 70 cm and 23 cm bands operate in FM mode and so can be received on any scanner that covers the bands. They are recognised by a periodic transmission of Morse code containing the callsign of the repeater, but with the declining use of this mode some may alternatively identify by a synthesised speech identification. Amateurs often call blind on repeaters and you may well hear the expression 'This is G8IYA listening through EA' meaning that amateur station G8IYA has accessed the repeater with callsign GB3EA and is awaiting any replies.

MARINE

The international VHF marine band as we saw in Chapter 6 is channelised. The standard procedure at commencement of a normal speech transmission on the band is to first put out a call on channel 16 – the calling and distress channel – requesting contact with a particular station. When that station replies, both then move to a working channel.

This method of operation means that at any time there might be hundreds of stations listening to channel 16, and so if any boat or ship needs help someone is usually bound to hear the call. A further advantage is that it enables shore stations to make general broadcasts to ships

A busy modern port needs radio communication to co-ordinate the movement and berthing of hundreds of trawlers, pleasure craft, ferries and cargo ships.

informing them that weather and safety warnings are about to be transmitted on a given channel. This method of initial calls is however being replaced by the GMDSS (Global Maritime Distress and Safety System) where initial transmissions employ a data transmission on channel 70 which contains information as to the nature of the call, and where appropriate designates a speech working channel for subsequent communications. However, the UK coastguard intend to also maintain an aural listening watch for some years on channel 16, and the owners of many pleasure craft will continue to use just speech communication.

Vessels licensed for marine RT and GMDSS are given a callsign comprising letters, numbers or both, depending on where the ship is registered. Generally the official callsign is only used when establishing link calls. For other contacts the vessel will only usually give the ship or boat's name.

Securité

Pronounced 'securitay' this word, repeated three times, precedes any broadcast transmission where there is reference to safety. Again, broadcasts telling ships that there is a securité message will be initially transmitted on channel 16, and where appropriate will give the channel to move to for the details.

Securité broadcasts usually concern navigational warnings. Typically they might inform vessels that a certain beacon or lighthouse is out of action, or they might warn of floating obstructions such as cargo washed off a ship's deck or a capsized vessel.

Some shore stations have the task of making regular broadcasts in busy shipping areas where there may be a need to pass frequent safety messages. Typical is Cherbourg Radio (channel 11) which transmits safety information every half hour for the southern part of the English Channel – possibly the busiest shipping zone in the world.

Weather

All coastal stations transmit regular weather forecasts and gale warnings. Again, forewarning of a weather forecast or gale warning will usually be made on channel 16 and the station will say which working channels will carry the forecast. More localised forecasts are made by some ports, using the same procedure as the coastal station.

Normally such forecasts are broadcast on the regular port operations channel.

Port operations

So far we have looked largely at the kind of transmissions and broadcasts that are from coastal stations covering a wide area. However, the marine VHF band is also used for other kinds of contact, in particular port operations. Many ports are busy places and some have traffic handling facilities almost as sophisticated as airports. Typical radio traffic concerns departure and arrival of ships, ferries and pleasure craft. Port controllers, for example, may have to hold some ships offshore until other ships have left and made space for them. They may be contacted by yachts wanting mooring spaces in marinas. Other tasks involve liaison with bodies such as customs and immigration officers.

Marina channels

There are channels specifically set aside for pleasure craft to communicate with marinas, for example to arrange berthing. These are channel M (this usually being channel 37 on suitably equipped marine radios), and increasingly channel 80 is also used as a marina channel to accommodate foreign craft whose radios may not have channel M. A further channel specific to the UK is channel M2, which is typically used by yacht clubs, and when an organised yacht race event is taking place this is the channel where much activity takes place.

Ship-to-ship

Several channels are set aside for ship-to-ship use. These are used for a variety of purposes, such as trawlermen discussing where the best catches are.

Emergencies

Britain has arguably the best marine emergency services in the world; its tradition as a seafaring nation is probably responsible for this. The waters around the British Isles are covered by lifeboat and coastguard stations, and support to these services comes from the Royal Air Force and Royal Navy. All services are on call to assist with emergencies at sea.

The first warning of an emergency concerning imminent danger to life will come with a Mayday call. This is internationally recognised and will either be made with a digital call on GMDSS or a speech call made on channel 16. Normally, a coastal station or port will receive the call and put the emergency services into action. Where coastal stations are out of range, a ship may well respond to the Mayday. During this time all traffic, other than emergency traffic, is supposed to cease on channel 16. No two emergencies are the same. In some instances it may just be a Pan-Pan or Securité message from a small vessel lost in fog and worried about running onto rocks. In such cases coastal stations might be able to offer position fixes by taking bearings on the transmissions of the vessel in danger by pinpointing the vessel's position. At the other end of the scale, the emergency might be a ship sinking in a storm.

AVIATION

The world of aviation is the winner when we come to judge it in terms of the number of expressions and jargon however, little of it is trivial. Aircraft crew cope with a variety of complex situations and may well be flying in and out of countries where air traffic controllers have little, if any, understanding of the English language.

Like the marine band the aircraft band is channelised, but the channels are referred to by their actual frequency and not by a channel number. The procedure for contacting a station is also very different. There is no common calling channel: a pilot wanting to call a ground station simply looks up the frequency and calls on it.

AIRCRAFT CALLSIGNS

To the uninitiated, listening-in on the airbands can often be a frustrating experience, not only because of the high level of jargon used by pilots and ground stations but also by the bewildering number of different callsigns that airlines and operators use. Callsigns will in fact fall into one of two categories. The first is the prefix which denotes the country or origin, the second is a self-assigned name registered with the authorities in the country of registration. One of these options will be used by all civil aircraft. Military aircraft using civilian airways might also use a code name. Typical examples being 'Reach' used by the United States Air Force and 'Ascot' used by the British Royal Air Force Transport Group.

First the country prefix. Table 7.2 shows the letters and numbers associated with the registration system for any particular country, but do heed that it is common practice to only give the full callsign on the first contact with a ground station. From then on the last two letters or digits of the callsign are all that are used. These registration prefixes are normally used by light aircraft – those that are privately owned and the smaller commercial operators – although there are instances where major airlines will use these as well.

Table 7.2 International aircraft callsign and registration prefixes

Prefix	Country	Prefix	Country	Prefix	Country
A2	Botswana	D	Germany	HR	Honduras
A3	Tonga	D2	Angola	HS	Thailand
A5	Bhutan	D4	Cape Verde Islands	HZ	Saudi Arabia
A6	United Arab Emirates	D6	Comores Is.	I	Italy
A7	Qatar	DQ	Fiji	J2	Djibouti
A9	Bahrain	EC	Spain	J3	Grenada
AP	Pakistan	EI/EJ	Eire	J5	Guinea Bissau
B	China/Taiwan	EL	Liberia	J6	St Lucia
CF	Canada	EP	Iran	J7	Dominica
CG	Canada	ET	Ethiopia	J8	St Vincent
C2	Nauru	F	France & French Terr.	JA	Japan
C3	Andorra	G	Great Britain	JY	Jordan
C5	Gambia	H4	Solomon Islands	LN	Norway
C6	Bahamas	HA	Hungarian Peoples Rep.	LQ/LV	Argentina
C9	Mozambique			LX	Luxembourg
CC	Chile	HB	Switzerland & Lichtenstein	LZ	Bulgaria
CN	Morocco			MI	Marshall Islands
CP	Bolivia	HC	Ecuador	N	USA
CR	Portugese Overseas Territories	HH	Haiti	OB	Peru
		HI	Dominican Republic	OD	Lebanon
CS	Portugal	HK	Columbia	OE	Austria
CU	Cuba	HL	South Korea	OH	Finland
CX	Uruguay	HP	Panama	OK	Czech Republic

Prefix	Country	Prefix	Country	Prefix	Country
OM	Slovak Republic	V8	Brunei	3X	Guinea
OO	Belgium	VH	Australia	4R	Sri Lanka
OY	Denmark	VN	Vietnam	4X	Israel
P	North Korea	VPF	Falkland Islands	5A	Libya
P2	Papua New Guinea	VPLKA	St Kitts Nevis	5B	Cyprus
PH	Netherlands	VPLLZ	St Kitts Nevis	5H	Tanzania
PK	Indonesia	VPLMA	Montserrat	5N	Nigeria
PJ	Netherlands Antilles	VPLUZ	Montserrat	5R	Madagascar
PP/PT	Brazil	VPLVA	Virgin Islands	5T	Mauritania
PZ	Surinam	VPLZZ	Virgin Islands	5U	Niger
RDPL	Laos	VQT	Turks & Caicos Is.	5V	Togo
RP	Phillipines	VRB	Bermuda	5W	Polynesia
S7	Seychelles	VRC	Cayman Islands	5X	Uganda
S2	Bangladesh	VRH	Hong Kong	5Y	Kenya
S9	Sao Tome	VT	India	6O	Somalia
SE	Sweden	XA/XB	Mexico	6V/6W	Senegal
SP	Poland	XC	Mexico	6Y	Jamaica
ST	Sudan	XT	Burkina Faso	7O	Yemen
SU	Egypt	XU	Kampuchea	7P	Lesotho
SX	Greece	XY/XZ	Burma	7Q	Malawi
T2	Tuvalu	YA	Afghanistan	7T	Algeria
T3	Kiribati	YI	Iraq	8P	Barbados
T7	San Marino	YJ	Vanuatu	8Q	Maldives
TC	Turkey	YK	Syria	8R	Guyana
TF	Iceland	YN	Nicaragua	9G	Ghana
TG	Guatemala	YR	Romania	9H	Malta
TI	Costa Rica	YS	El Salvador	9J	Zambia
TJ	Cameroon	YV	Venezuela	9K	Kuwait
TL	Central Africa	Z	Zimbabwe	9L	Sierra Leone
TR	Gabon	ZA	Albania	9M	Malaysia
TS	Tunisia	ZK	New Zealand	9N	Nepal
TT	Chad	ZP	Paraguay	9Q	Congo
TU	Ivory Coast	ZS	South Africa	9U	Burundi
TY	Benin	3A	Monaco	9V	Singapore
TZ	Mali	3B	Mauritius	9XR	Rwanda
V2	Antigua	3C	Equatorial Guinea	9Y	Trinidad & Tobago
V3	Belize	3D	Swaziland		

Callsigns

If the full callsign consists of letters only then you can be almost certain that the callsign being used is the standard country prefix followed by the aircraft registration. The vast majority of countries use two, three or four letter groups after the country prefix but there are a few exceptions and the notable ones are:

United States of America	N followed by numbers or a mix of numbers and letters.
Japan	JA followed by a 4-digit number.
Venezuela	YV followed by a 3-digit number then suffixed with a single letter.
China/Taiwan	B followed by a 3- or 4-digit number.
Cuba	CU-T followed by a 4-digit number.
Columbia	HK followed by a 4-digit number suffixed with X.
Korea	HL followed by a 4-digit number.

All civilian aircraft have a registration. Generally, privately owned light aircraft or those operated as air-taxis will use their registration as their radio callsign. Normal procedure for making contact with the ground station will be to give the full callsign. The controller will reply, perhaps, referring to the aircraft by the full callsign, in which case the pilot will again, when transmitting, use the full callsign. At some stage though, for the sake of brevity, the approach controller will just use the last two letters and from then on the pilot will do the same.

Larger aircraft, such as those used on regular passenger-carrying routes, may use the same type of callsign, or a special callsign based on the airline's name and typically may also use the flight number for that service. Again the ground controller will probably, at some stage, abbreviate this and just use the number: from then on the aircrew will do the same. Numbers preceded by the word 'Ascot' denote the callsign of a British military aircraft flying on a civilian route. The USAF equivalent is the pre-fix 'Mac'.

Landing instructions

The first contact an aircraft will have with an airfield is usually on the approach frequency. After transmitting on the frequency and identifying the aircraft, the pilot usually gives aircraft position and altitude. The approach controller then transmits information relating to airfield barometric pressure (QFE), the wind direction and speed, the runway in use (runways are always identified by the compass heading needed to land on them), and details of other aircraft in the landing pattern or about to take off. Temperature and visibility in kilometres may be also given. If the weather is bad the RVR (runway visual range) may be referred to. The pilot needs to know the QFE (sometimes just called the 'fox echo') so that the aircraft's altimeter may be set so that it will read zero feet at runway level. Other information such as runway state (if affected by rain, ice or snow) may be transmitted, followed by instructions to remain at present altitude or start descending to circuit height (often about 1000 feet). Some of this information the pilot will repeat back.

As the aircraft gets closer to the airport there will come a stage where the approach controller instructs the pilot to change to the tower frequency. The pilot always repeats the frequency to be changed to: this is standard procedure when changing frequency at any point in a flight. Now the pilot calls the tower and again will give his position and altitude. The aircraft may be making a straight-in approach, i.e. arriving at the airfield in line with the runway or he may be 'joining the circuit'. The circuit is an imaginary path around the airfield in the form of a racetrack. It can be in a left-hand or right-hand direction and, once joined, the pilot will report at various stages such as downwind leg, base leg and finals. Finals occur at a given distance from the runway and the pilot will always tell the controller when the aircraft is one mile out. Throughout this stage of the flight the pilot will be given various instructions and updated QFE, wind speed and direction information. At any stage of the approach the pilot may be told to divert course because the controller cannot yet fit him in with other traffic. The instruction may be to briefly orbit over a given position, or to fly out further to a given point and then rejoin the landing pattern. Once on the ground the pilot may be told to change frequency yet again (particularly at larger airfields), this time to speak to the ground handler. Here, instructions on which taxiways to use and where to park the aircraft will be given.

Table 7.3 Airline callsigns

Callsign	Operator	Country
Aceforce	NATO Command	Europe military
Ace Air	Air Cargo Express	USA
Actair	Air Charter and Travel	UK
Aeradio	International Aeradio	UK
Aero	United States Army	US military
Aero Lloyd	Aero Lloyd	Germany
Aeroflot	Aeroflot	Russia
Aeromar Com	Aeromaritime d'Affretement	France
Aeromaritime	Aeromaritime	France
Aeromexico	Aeromexico	Mexico
Aeronaut	Cranfield Institute of Technology	UK government
Aeroperu	Aeroperu	Peru
Aeroswede	Syd Aero	Sweden
Afro	Affretair	Zimbabwe
Airafric Air	Afrique	Ivory Coast
Air America	Air America	USA
Air Atlantis	Air Atlantis	Portugal
Air Belgium	Air Belgium	Belgium
Air BVI	Air BVI	BVI

Callsign	Operator	Country
Air Canada	Air Canada	Canada
Aircal	Air Caledonie	France
Air Falcon	Europe Falcon Service	France
Air Ferry	British Air Ferries	UK
Air Force One	US President	US military
Air Force Two	US Vice-President	US military
Air France	Air France	France
Air Freighter	Aeron International	USA
Air Hong Kong	Air Hong Kong	Hong Kong
Air India	Air India	India
Air Lanka	Air Lanka	Sri Lanka
Air London	Air London	UK
Air Mauritius	Air Mauritius	Mauritius
Airmil	Spanish Air Force	Spain
Air Portugal	Air Portugal	Portugal
Air Rwanda	Air Rwanda	Rwanda
Air Services	Austrian Air Services	Austria
Air Tara	Air Tara	Eire
Airtax	Birmingham Aviation	UK
Air Zimbabwe	Air Zimbabwe	Zimbabwe
Airafric	Air Afrique	Ivory Coast
Airbiz	Maersk Commuter	Denmark
Airbridge	Air Bridge Carriers	UK
Aircargo	Intavia	UK
Airgo	Airgo	UK
Airmove	Skywork	UK
Airnav	Air Navigation and Trading	UK
Alisarda	Alisarda	Italy
Alitali	Alitalia	Italy
All Nippo	All Nippon	Japan
American	American Airlines	USA
Amtran	American Trans-Air	USA
Anglo	Anglo Cargo	UK
Argentine	Aerolineas Argentinas	Argentina
Armyair	Army Air Corps	UK military
Ascot	RAF 1 Group Air Transport	UK military
Aspro	Intereuropean Airways	UK
Atlantic	Air Atlantique	UK
Augusta	Augusta Airways	Australia
Austrian	Austrian Airlines	Austria
Aviaco	Aviaco	Spain
Avianca	Avianca	Colombia
Ayline	Aurigny Air Services	UK
Backer	British Charter	UK
Bafair	Belgian Air Force	Belgium
Bafjet	British Air Ferries Business Jets	UK
Bahrain One	The Amiri Flight	Bahrain
Bailair	Balair	Switzerland
Balkan	Balkan Bulgarian Airlines	Bulgaria

Callsign	Operator	Country
Batman	Ratioflug	Germany
Bangladesh	Bangladesh Biman	Bangladesh
Beaupair	Aviation Beauport	UK
Beeline	Biggin Hill Executive	UK
Birmex	Birmingham European	UK
Biztravel	Business Air Travel	UK
Beatours	British Airtours	UK
Blackbox	Bedford Royal Aircraft Establishment	UK government
Blackburn	British Aerospace (Scampton)	UK
Bluebird	Finnaviation	Finland
Bodensee	Delta Air	Germany
Botswana	Air Botswana	Botswana
Braethens	Braethens SAFE	Norway
Bristol	British Aerospace (Bristol)	UK
Britannia	Britannia Airways	UK
Britanny	Brit Air	France
British Island	British Island Airways	UK
Brunei	Royal Brunei Airlines	Brunei
Busy Bee	Busy Bee	Norway
Camair	Cameroon Airlines	Cameroon
Canada	Worldways Canadian	Canada
Canadian	Canadian Airlines	Canada
Canforce	Canadian Air Force	Canada
Cargo	Safair Freighters	South Africa
Cargolux	Cargolux	Luxembourg
Cathay	Cathay Pacific Airways	Hong Kong
Cayman	Cayman Airways	Cayman Islands
Cedar Jet	Middle East Airlines	Lebanon
Chad	Chad Air Services	Chad
Channex	Channel Express	UK
China	CAAC	China
City	KLM City Hopper	Holland
Clansman	Airwork Limited	UK
Conair	Conair	Denmark
Condor	Condor Flugdienst	Germany
Contactair	Contactair	Germany
Continental	Continental Airlines	USA
Corsair	Corsair	France
Crossair	Crossair	Switzerland
Cubana	Cubana	Cuba
Cyprus	Cyprus Airways	Cyprus
Dantax	Aalborg Airtaxi	Belgium
Databird	Air Nigeria	Nigeria
Dash	Air Atlantic	UK
Delta	Delta Air Lines	USA
Deltair	Delta Air Transport	Belgium
DLT	DLT	Germany
Dominair	Aerolineas Dominicanes	Dominican Republic

145

Callsign	Operator	Country
Dragon	Welsh Airways	UK
Dynamite	Dynamic Air	Holland
Easyjet	Easyjet	UK
Egyptair	Egyptair	Egypt
El Al	El Al	Israel
Elite	Air 3000	Canada
Emery	Emery Worldwide	USA
Emirates	Emirate Airlines	UAE
Espania	CTA Espania	Spain
Ethiopian	Ethiopian Airlines	Ethiopia
Euralair	Euralair	France
Euroair	Euroair Transport	UK
Eurotrans	European Air Transport	Belgium
Evergreen	Evergreen International	USA
Excalibur	Air Exel	UK
Executive	Extra Executive Transport	Germany
Express	Federal Express	USA
Falcon Jet	Falcon Jet Centre	UK
Ferranti	Ferranti Ltd	UK
Finnair	Finnair	Finland
Flamingo	Nurnberger Flugdienst	Germany
Food	Food Brokers Limited	UK
Fordair	Ford Motor Company	UK
Foyl	Air Foyle	UK
Fred Olsen	Fred Olsen Air Transport	Norway
Gatwick Air	Gatwick Air Taxis	UK
Gauntlet	Boscombe Down (MOD)	UK military
German Cargo	German Cargo	Germany
Germania	Germania	Germany
Ghana	Ghana Airways	Ghana
Gibair	GB Airways Limited	UK
Golf November	Air Gabon	Gabon
Granite	Business Air	UK
Greenlandair	Gronlandsfly	Denmark
Gulf Air	Gulf Air	Oman
Guyair	Guyana Airways	Guyana
Hapag-Lloyd	Hapag-Lloyd	Germany
Hatair	Hatfield Executive Aviation	UK
Hawker	British Aerospace (Dunsfold)	UK
Hunting	Hunting Surveys	UK
Iberian	Iberia	Spain
Iceair	Icelandair	Iceland
Indonesian	Garuda Indonesian Airways	Indonesia
Interflug	Interflug	Germany
Iranair	Iran Air	Iran
Iraqi	Iraqi Airways	Iraq
Janus	Janus Airways	UK
Japanair	Japan Air Lines	Japan
Jetset	Air 2000	UK
Joker	Germania	Germany

Callsign	Operator	Country
Jordanian	Royal Jordanian Airline	Jordan
KLM	KLM Royal Dutch Airlines	Holland
Karair	Kar-Air	Finland
Kenya	Kenya Airlines	Kenya
Kestrel	Airtours	UK
Kilo Mike	Air Malta	Malta
Kilroe	Air Kilro	UK
Kittyhawk	Queen's Flights	UK military
Koreanair	Korean Air	Korea
Kuwaiti	Kuwait Airways	Kuwait
Leopard	Queen's Flights	UK military
Libair	Libyan Arab Airlines	Libya
Lion	British International Helicopters	UK
Lovo	Lovaux Limited	UK
Lufthansa	Lufthansa	Germany
Luxair	Luxair	Luxembourg
Macline	McAlpine Aviation Limited	UK
Madair	Air Madagascar	Madagascar
Maerskair	Maersk Air	Denmark
Malawi	Air Malawi	Malawi
Malaysian	Malaysian Airlines System	Malaya
Malev	Malev	Hungary
Mamair	Marine and Aviation Management	UK
Mann	Alan Mann Helicopters	UK
Marocair	Royal Air Maroc	Morocco
Martinair	Martinair	Holland
Mediterranean	Mediterranean Express	UK
Merlin	Rolls-Royce Military	UK
Metman	Meteorological Research Flight	UK government
Metro	Bohnstedt Petersen Aviation	Denmark
Midas	Milford Docks Air Services	UK
Midland	British Midland Airways	UK
Midwing	Airborne of Sweden	Sweden
Mike Romeo	Air Mauritania	Mauritania
Minair	CAA Flying Unit	UK government
Minerve	Minerve	France
Monarch	Monarch Airlines	UK
Nationair	Nation Air	Canada
National	Airmore Aviation	UK
Navy	Royal Navy	UK military
Neatax	Northern Executive Aviation	UK
Netherlands	Royal Netherlands Air Force	Holland
Netherlines	Netherlines	Holland
New Zealand	Air New Zealand	New Zealand
Newpin	British Aerospace (Hawarden)	UK
Nigerian	Nigerian Airways	Nigeria
Nightflight	Night Flight	UK
Norseman	Norsk Air	Norway
Northair	Northern Air Taxis	UK

147

Callsign	Operator	Country
Northwest	Northwest Orient	USA
November Lima	Air Liberia	Liberia
November Papa	Heavylift Cargo Airlines	UK
Nugget	Farnborough Royal Aircraft Establishment	UK government
Olympic	Olympic Airways	Greece
Orange	Air Holland	Holland
Orion	Orion Airways	UK
Overnight	Russow Aviation	Germany
Palmair	Palmair	UK
Pakistan	Pakistan International	Pakistan
Para	Army Parachute Centre	UK military
Paraguaya	Lineas Aereas Paraguayas (LAP)	Paraguay
Partnair	Partnair	Norway
Pearl	Oriental Pearl Airways	UK
Philair	Philips Aviation Services	Holland
Philippine	Philippine Airlines	Philippines
Plum	PLM Helicopters	UK
Police	Police Aviation Services	UK
Pollot	Polski Linie Lotnicze (LOT)	Poland
Port	Skyworld Airlines	USA
Puma	Phoenix Aviation	UK
Qantas	Qantas	Australia
Quebec Tango	Aer Turas	Eire
Racal	Racal Avionics	UK
Rafair	Royal Air Force	UK military
Rainbow	Queen's Flights	UK military
Reach	USAF Air Mobility Command	US military
Regal	Crown Air	Canada
Rescue	RAF Rescue	UK military
Richair	Rich International	USA
Rogav	Rogers Aviation	UK
Rushton	Flight Refuelling Limited	UK
Sabena	Sabena	Belgium
Sam	USAF Special Air Mission	US military
Saudia	Saudia	Saudi Arabia
Scandanavian	Scandanavian Airlines System	Sweden
Scanwings	Maimo Aviation	Sweden
Seychelles	Air Seychelles	Seychelles
Shamrock	Air Lingus	Ireland
Short	Short Brothers	UK
Sierra India	Arab Wings	Jordan
Singapore	Singapore Airlines	Singapore
Sky Express	Salair	Sweden
Somalair	Somali Airlines	Somalia
Southern	Air Southern Air Transport	USA
Spantax	Spantax	Spain
Special	Metropolitan Police Air Unit	UK
Speedbird	British Airways	UK
Speedfox	Jetair Aps	Denmark
Speedpack	International Parcel Express	USA

Callsign	Operator	Country
Springbok	South African Airways	South Africa
Starjet	Novair	UK
Stellair	Stellair	France
Sterling	Sterling Airways	Denmark
Sudanair	Sudan Airways	Sudan
Swedair	Swedair	Sweden
Swedeline	Linjeflyg	Sweden
Swedic	Swedish Air Force	Sweden
Swissair	Swissair	Switzerland
Syrianair	Syrian Arab Airlines	Syria
Tarnish	British Aerospace (Warton)	UK
Tarom	Tarom	Romania
Teastar	Trans European	UK
Tee Air	Tower Air	UK
Tennant	British Aerospace (Prestwick)	UK
Tester	Empire Test Pilots School	UK military
Thai Inter	Thai International Airlines	Thailand
Tibbet	British Aerospace (Hatfield)	UK
Tiger	Flying Tiger Line	USA
Tradewinds	Tradewinds Airways	UK
Trans Arabian	Trans Arabian Air Transport	Sudan
Trans Europe	Trans Europe Air Charter	UK
Trans-Med	Trans Mediterranean Airways	Lebanon
Transway	TEA Basle	Switzerland
Transworld	Trans World Airlines	USA
Tunair	Tunis-Air	Tunisia
Turkair	Turk Hava Yollari (THY)	Turkey
Tyrolean	Tyrolean Airways	Austria
Uganda	Uganda Airlines	Uganda
Uni-Air	Uni-Air	France
Unicorn	Queen's Flights	UK military
UTA	UTA	France
Varig	Varig	Brazil
Vectis	Pilatus Britten-Norman	UK
Viasa	Viasa	Venezuela
Victor Kilo	Airbus Industrie	France
Victor Yankee	Air Belgium	Belgium
Viking	Scanair	Sweden
Virgin	Virgin Atlantic	UK
Wardair	Wardair	Canada
Watchdog	Ministry of Agriculture, Fisheries & Food	UK government
West Indian	British West Indian Airways	Trinidad
White Star	Star Air	Denmark
Wigwam	CSE Aviation	UK
Woodair	Woodgate Air Services	UK
World	World Airways	USA
Worldways	Worldways Canada	Canada
Yemeni	Yemenia Airways	Yemen
Zambia	Zambia Airways	Zambia
Zap	Titan Airways	UK

Suffixes

Occasionally a suffix will be added to the group of numbers following the above callsign to denote a special characteristic of the flight. These are usually as follows although it should be noted that British Airways operate a different system.

A Added where a flight has been doubled up so that two aircraft are using the same prefix and numerals (for example one aircraft will be suffixed A and the other B).

F Aircraft carrying freight only.

P Aircraft positioning to another location with no passengers on board.

Q Aircraft details have been changed to a standard flight plan (for example the regular aircraft has been substituted with another type).

T Training flight.

X Allocated by controllers to avoid confusion when two aircraft have identical numbers even though their prefixes may differ.

Heavy tells controllers that the aircraft is a wide-bodied type.

Private aircraft and those operated by smaller operators such as air taxis may well use just their registration. In Britain this will consist of the prefix G followed by up to four letters. On establishing first contact with a controller the pilot will give his call sign in full. For instance G-APTY would be Golf-Alpha Papa Tango Yankee. However, the controller may well abbreviate this to Golf-Tango Yankee or even just Tango Yankee.

SRA and PAR radar let-down

Occasionally, in bad visibility, a pilot may need to be talked-down. Surveillance Radar Approach (SAR) may be used to give the pilot precise instructions to reach the end of the runway. Normally, the airfield has a special frequency for this and once the pilot has established contact with the controller there is a point when the controller tells the pilot not to acknowledge further instructions. From then on, the controller gives the pilot a running commentary on the aircraft's position in relation to an imaginary line drawn outwards from the runway, known as the centre-line. Compass headings may be given to the pilot, to steer the aircraft, in order to get on to the centre-line. Other information given tells the pilot how far the aircraft is from the runway and what height it should be at. At a point about half a mile from the runway, the controller announces that the approach is complete. If the pilot cannot see the runway at this stage the approach must be abandoned for another, or the aircraft is diverted to another airfield. Failing to touch-down results in a 'go-around' (formerly an 'overshoot).

Precision Radar Approach (PAR) is similar, but also tells the pilot altitude and whether or not the aircraft is on the glide slope.

Startup

The procedure at the start of a flight varies from airfield to airfield. On smaller airfields the pilot may start the aircraft and then ask for take-off instructions. The ground controller transmits details of which runway is in use, QFE and wind, then instructs the pilot to start taxiing to a holding point just before the end of the runway. Once the runway is clear, the controller allows the aircraft to take off and relays other instructions such as which height to climb to and when the aircraft can start turning on course.

At bigger airfields, particularly those in busy flight areas, the procedure may be far more complicated and will depend to some extent on whether the flight is VFR (visual flight rules) or IFR (instrument flight rules). The first, VFR, is where an aircraft flies solely by dead reckoning. In other words, the pilot navigates by using a compass and a map, looking out of the aircraft windows for landmarks. The second, IFR, is where the pilot uses radionavigation and instruments to cover the route. Most commercial flights are IFR and such flights are always along designated airways routes. Prior to a flight the pilot files a flight plan with Air Traffic Control which is electronically distributed to controllers on the aircraft's route, who are then aware of the type of aircraft, altitude requested and destination. At commencement of the flight the pilot informs the tower that all is ready. At this stage the controller may well only say the aircraft is clear to startup and, perhaps, will give the temperature. Once the pilot informs the controller the aircraft is ready for take-off, taxiing instructions, the QFE, the runway in use and the wind details are all given. At this stage or shortly after clearance is given to the pilot, detailing destination, the airways to use and altitudes.

In the UK airways are identified by colours (red, blue, green, white, amber) with a number. After the actual take-off, the aircraft may be handed over to another controller, such as approach, before the pilot is finally told to contact airways or information services.

Airways

Busy air routes, such as those over Europe, are divided up into countries and regions which have central control points for all the air routes in the sectors. Although VFR flights at low altitudes can, by and large, choose the course they fly, this is not the case at higher altitudes in the airways.

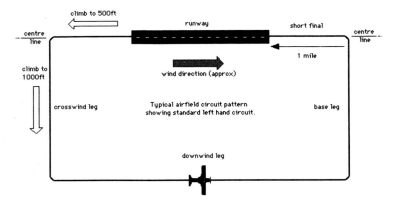

Figure 7.1 Typical airfield circuit pattern showing standard left-hand circuit.

Now we are in the realms of controlled airspace and pilots must fly along a certain course at a certain height. The airways are marked at regular points, and where they cross, by beacons on the ground. These are used for navigation purposes and also form what are known as compulsory reporting points: as the aircraft passes over a beacon the pilot must report to the sector controller, giving the name of the beacon, flight level (at higher altitudes the height is abbreviated, e.g. 10,000 feet becomes flight level one-zero-zero), and forward estimate time for the next reporting point. These points are referred to by the name of the place where the beacon is sited.

Towards the end of the journey the pilot may be given a fairly complex set of instructions. Landing at major airports like London Heathrow may, at busy times, involve joining the stack – an imaginary spiral staircase in the sky. The aircraft joins at the top and flies a racetrack-shaped circuit, slowly dropping to different flight levels until, at the bottom, it is routed to the airfield.

Flight information

Everything above 25,000 feet is controlled airspace (in some regions airspace below that altitude is controlled, too). Pilots can obtain details of traffic movements in the region from the Upper-flight Information Region (UIR) service. Below that level, information is provided by the Flight Information Region (FIR) service. Note that both the UIR and FIR are advisory services: they provide information for pilots but do not control the movement of aircraft. A further advisory service is available for small aircraft on VFR flights: Lower Airspace Radar Service (LARS). The facility is provided by the various Military Aerodrome Traffic Zones (MATZ) up

(Photographs by Ian
Doyle)

and down the country. Again, they do not control flights but merely offer information regarding other aircraft in the area.

Company frequencies

Most airlines use company frequencies. Any of these frequencies, however, might be used by several airline operators to contact company ground stations. An example of the use of company frequencies could be when an aircraft wishes to contact the operations department of the company base at the destination airfield, in order to give the estimated time of arrival or request special services such as wheelchairs for invalid passengers. Other messages may concern servicing required on the aircraft: instruments may need adjusting, or there may be minor technical problems that engineers will need to correct before the aircraft takes off again.

GLOSSARY

The following list of abbreviations and expressions are regularly used during typical transmissions between ground and air.

Abort   Abandon (i.e. abandon take-off).

AFIS   Airfield flight information service.

AIREP   Report for position and weather in flight.

Airway   Defined flight path.

AMSL   Above mean sea level.

APU   Auxiliary power unit (backup when engines are off).

ASDA   Runway accelerated stop distance.

ASI   Air speed indicator.

ATA   Actual time of arrival.

ATC   Air traffic control.

ATIS   Automatic terminal information service.

Avgas   Aviation grade petrol.

Avionics   Aircraft electronics.

Backtrack   Taxi back down the runway.

Beacon   Station transmitting continuous navigation signal.

CAT   Clear air turbulence.

CBs   Cumulo nimbus (thunder clouds).

Conflicting   Conflicting traffic, etc, possible collision course.

Decimal   Decimal point as in frequency, e.g. 128.65 MHz.

Cav-OK   Ceiling and visibility are good.

DF   Direction finding by radio.

DME   Distance measuring equipment.

Drift   Lateral movement off desired track.

ETA   Estimated time of arrival.

FIR   Flight information region.

Flameout   Total power loss on jet or turbo prop engine.

Gear   Undercarriage.

Glide-path   Line of descent on landing.

GMC   Ground movement controller.

GMT   Greenwich mean time.

Go around   Overshoot runway and re-join circuit.

GPU   Ground power unit.

Greens   Landing gear down and locked indicators.

Homer   Homing beacon.

IAS   Indicated air speed.

IFR   Instrument flight rules.

ILS   Instrument landing system.

IMC   Instrument meteorological conditions.

JET   A1 jet and turbo-prop fuel (kerosene).

Knots   Nautical miles per hour.

LARS   Lower airspace radar service.

Localiser   Glide-path beacon.

Mach   Speed in relation to the speed of sound.

MATZ   Military aerodrome traffic zone.

METAR   Meterological report (not a forecast).

Navaid   Navigational aid.

NavCom   Combined communication and navigation radio.

Navex   Navigation exercise (training flight).

NDB   Non-directional beacon.

NOTAM   Notice to airmen.

Okta   An eighth. Used to denote cloud density.

Ops   Operations.

Orbit   Fly in a circle.

Overshoot   No longer used, see Go around.

Pax   Passengers (e.g. 64 pax on board).

PAR   Precision approach radar.

PPO   Prior permission only (restricted airfields).

QDM   Magnetic heading.

QFE   Barometric pressure at aerodrome.

QNH   Barometric pressure at sea level.

Roll-out   Stopping distance after touchdown.

RSR   Route surveillance radar.

RVR   Runway visual range.

SAR   Search and rescue.

SELCAL   Selective calling system (activates radio by code).

SID   Standard instrument departure.

SIG   Significant.

SitRep   Situation report.

Squawk   Switch transponder on.

Squawk ident   Select identification mode on transponder.

SRE   Surveillance radar element.

STOL   Short take-off and landing.

Stratus   Low misty cloud (often obscures runway approach).

TAI   True air speed indicator.

TACAN   Tactical air navigator.

TAF   Terminal area forecast.

TAR   Terminal area radar.

TAS   True airspeed.

TMA   Terminal control area.

Traffic   Aircraft in flight.

UIR   Upper flight information region.

US   Unserviceable.

UTC   Universal time constant (GMT).

VASI   Runway lights angled to give a visual glide slope.

VFR   Visual flight rules.

VMC   Visual meteorological conditions.

VOLMET   Continuous weather forecast.

VOR   VHF omni-direction range beacon.

VSI   Vertical speed indicator (rate of climb).

VTOL   Vertical take-off and landing.

WX   Weather.

SPACE STATIONS

Due to its low-earth orbit, the Mir space station can be heard with just a handheld scanner used outdoors with its set-top helical, the engineering voice downlink on 143.625 MHz FM is a very strong signal. It orbits the Earth about every 90 minutes, and a satellite tracking program with up- to-date Mir Keplers loaded will tell you exactly when it's within range of your location. The cosmonauts also use amateur radio in the 2m and 70cm bands as recreation, usually at weekends and during their rest periods and there's also an amateur radio packet bulletin board operational from the space station. The International Space Station, still due to be constructed as this is written, will also have an amateur radio station on board as well plenty of radio communication activity between the station, other vessels and the ground.

NASA SHUTTLES

Three UHF frequencies have been used by the NASA shuttles over the years but it should be noted that on some missions, the communications have been restricted to frequencies which are outside the range of ordinary scanners. However, UHF communications are heard on some flights, particularly those involving spacewalks (Extra Vehicular Activity – EVA). It must be stressed that shuttle communications are unlikely to be heard on a scanner which is simply being used with an ordinary discone antenna. Crossed dipoles, or preferably a crossed yagi with its elements phased for circular polarisation, designed for the frequency together with a masthead preamplifier are advisable for best results. The following abbreviations are ones commonly used during the lift-off phase (frequently rebroadcast via the media) and during some stages of the flight.

AFSCN   Air Force Satellite Control Network.

ALT   Approach for landing test programme.

AMU   Astronaut manouvering unit.

APS   Alternate payload specialist.

APU   Auxiliary power unit.

ASE   Airborne support equipment.

ATE   Automatic test equipment.

ATO   Abort to orbit.

BFC   Backup flight control.

CAPCOM   Capsule Communicator.

CCAFS   Cape Canaveral Air Force Station.

CCMS   Checkout, control and monitor sub-systems.

CDMS   Command and data management systems officer.

CDR   Commander.

CDS   Central data systems.

CIC   Crew interface coordinator.

CIE   Communications interface equipment.

CTS   Call to stations.

DCC   Data computation complex.

DCS   Display control system.

DIG   Digital image generation.

DFI   Development flight instrumentation.

DFRF   Dryden Flight Research Facility.

DMC   Data management coordinator.

DOD   Department of Defence.

DPS   Data processing system.

EAFB   Edwards Air Force Base.

ECLSS   Environmental control and life support system.

EMU   Extra vehicular mobility unit.

ESMC   Eastern Space and Missile Center.

ET   External tank.

EVA   Extra vehicular activity.

FAO   Flight activities officer.

F/C   Flight controller.

FD   Flight director.

FDO   Flight dynamics officer.

FOD   Flight Operations Directorate.

FOE   Flight operations engineer.

FOSO   Flight operations scheduling officer.

FR   Firing room.

FRC   Flight control room.

FRCS   Forward reaction control system.

FRF   Flight readiness firing.

FRR   Flight readiness review.

GAS   Getaway special.

GC   Ground control.

GDO   Guidance officer.

GLS   Ground launch sequencer.

GN   Ground network.

GNC   Guidance, navigation and control systems engineer.

GPC   General purpose computer.

GSE   Ground support equipment.

GSFC   Goddard Space Flight Center.

IG   Inertial guidance.

ILS   Instrument landing system.

IMF   In-flight maintenance.

INCO   Instrumentation and communications officer.

IUS   Inertial upper stage.

IVA   Intra vehicular activity.

JSC   Johnson Space Center.

KSC   Kennedy Space Center.

LC   Launch complex.

LCC   Launch control centre.

LCS   Launch control system.

LOX   Liquid oxygen.

LPS   Launch processing system.

MCC   Mission control centre.

MD   Mission director.

ME   Main engine.

MECO   Main engine cut-off.

MET   Mission elapsed time.

MLS   Microwave landing system.

MOD   Mission operations directorate.

MOP   Mission operations plan.

MPS   Main propulsion system.

MS   Mission specialist.

MSCI   Mission scientist.

MSFC   Marshall Space Flight Center.

NASCOM   NASA Communications Network.

NOCC   Network Operations Control Center.

NSRS   NASA safety reporting system.

OAA   Orbiter Access Arm.

OC   Operations coordinator.

OFI Operational flight instrumentation.

OMS Orbiter manoeuvering system.

PDRS Payload deployment and retrieval system.

PLT Pilot

POD Payload operations director.

PS Payload specialist.

RMS Remote manipulator system.

RTLS Return to launch site.

SIP Standard interface panel.

SLF Shuttle landing facility.

SN Space network.

SPOC Shuttle portable on-board computer.

SRB Solid rocket booster.

SRM Solid rocket motor.

SSC Stennis Space Center.

SSCP Small self-contained payload.

SSME Space shuttle main engines.

SSP Standard switch panel.

TACAN Tactical air navigation.

TAL Trans-Atlantic abort landing.

TDRS Tracking data and relay satellite.

WSMC Western Space and Missile Center.

8 Satellites on your scanner

Many people are often amazed when they find they can hear signals from space on their scanner, whether these are voice transmissions from astronauts or weather fax transmissions which a PC running suitable software can instantly convert into picture format.

Above us at this very moment, a network of satellites is beaming signals to us – pictures of our country, our continent, and even the entire globe as seen from their 'eyes' in outer space. Some of these satellites orbit the Earth a few hundred miles above us, sending us close-up images, others stay around 23,000 miles above us in geostationary orbit, transmit-

Received weather satellite picture using Timestep weather satellite program.

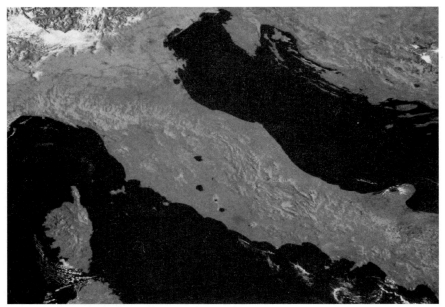

Another received weather satellite picture using Timestep weather satellite program.

ting images of their entire visible 'disc' as well as various sectionalised areas.

Try setting your scanner to search across 137–138 MHz one afternoon with your aerial having a clear 'view' of the sky above. Even with just a set-top whip, you will soon hear the mysterious sounding bleeps from one of the NOAA (US) or Cosmos/Meteor low-earth orbiting satellites as they pass otherwise silently above you.

STARTING OUT

So what do you need to decode these bleeps, and transform them into visual images? If you have a computer as well as your scanner you already have most of what you need. There are several software packages available for PCs which normally operate with either a simple plug-in interface or by using the PC's sound card.

Many beginners start by receiving the low-earth orbiting satellites. You can, if you wish, simply take 'pot luck' and see what you can receive at any time, using a simple fixed aerial system such as crossed dipoles. You can alternatively run a satellite pass prediction program on your computer to tell you exactly which satellite is coming over and when.

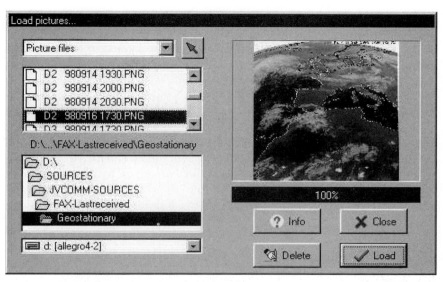

This PC-based program, JVCOMM32 uses your PC's sound card as the interface for weather satellite decoding.

RECEIVERS

Although many low-cost scanners can give you a start, weather satellites use higher deviation than normal terrestrial two-way radio signals. Your receiver needs to be able to cope with a wider than normal FM deviation, plus up to ±3 kHz of Doppler shift (the effect of increasing and decreasing frequency with movement towards and away from you) in the case of the orbiting satellites. A bandwidth of around 50 kHz is ideal, but if you have a sensitive receiver then the Wide FM mode on your scanner may give acceptable results, although this is often rather too wide. Another problem with this is breakthrough of paging signal interference in the UK from high power transmitters operating in the adjacent paging band. The best way is to make sure your scanner has a suitable IF bandwidth – a number of scanners for both the 137 MHz and 1691 MHz ranges have this facility.

AERIALS

For reception of the orbiting 137 MHz satellites, a vertical whip or discone will work but it won't give you the best results. A pair of crossed dipoles, phased for circular polarisation are ideal, and you can improve the gain by using a pair of reflector elements beneath these, or of course try adding a masthead preamp if you don't suffer from other strong signals.

For reception of the geostationary satellites such as Meteosat over Europe (at 0 deg longitude) or the GOES series on the Western hemisphere, a higher gain aerial is needed – a long yagi is a popular choice. In the UK this needs to be aimed due south at an elevation of around 30 degrees. Alternatively, a 1m dish can be used, fitted with either a probe feed, commonly home-made inside a large coffee tin, or a simple dipole element at the focal point. Larger dishes give greater gain and are suitable for reception of the high-quality primary user data transmitted (see later). An aerial-mounted preamplifier is almost essential to overcome coax feeder losses at these frequencies.

DECODING

Both visible and infra-red images are transmitted by the satellites as well as other types, but don't confuse weather fax decoding (from HF signals) with weather satellite decoding (from VHF/UHF signals), the two are different. Some PC-based programs even allow you to artificially colour the images, to replicate blue sea and green land for example.

For orbiting satellite pass prediction, again plenty of software is available, including some as shareware. For accuracy these require you to enter up-to-date Keplerian elements to allow for minor changes in the satellites' orbits – these are freely available from various sources such as the NASA site on the Internet.

All the weather satellites use automatic picture transmission (APT), which varies the amplitude of a 2400 Hz tone which is then transmitted using FM. Hence you can use the same decoder for either orbiting or geostationary satellite decoding, although most software has a number of preset modes to cater for the slight differences in the format of these.

High resolution picture transmission (HRPT) and primary data user system (PDUS) formats are also transmitted in digital form. These were once limited to professional users, but end-user systems for the reception of these are now available for keen devotees who would like to receive high resolution images from the satellites.

The Meteosat images you receive on APT are processed images from a ground station, with country contours added to help identification. Images of the whole of Europe are transmitted every half hour, plus four visible close-ups of Europe every hour during daylight hours, the entire visible 'disc' sixteen times a day, plus other sections at intervals including infra-red retransmissions taken from the GOES satellite over the USA.

SPEECH COMMUNICATIONS

There are a great number of other man-made satellites orbiting the Earth: some of these stay permanently in space (communication, weather and navigation vehicles); others, such as the American space shuttle, only stay up for a pre-determined period. The latter are usually manned with crews – astronauts in the case of the Americans, cosmonauts in the case of the Russians. For the scanner user, not all forms of transmission can be received from these space vehicles as many of the frequencies used are in the SHF band (3–30 GHz). However some VHF and UHF frequencies are used and those likely to be of interest to scanner users are some of the voice communications for the astronauts/cosmonauts, and amateur communications relays.

DATA TRANSMISSIONS

Many of the space allocations shown in Tables 6.1 and 6.2 do not contain voice transmissions. Many satellites transmit streams of data from on-board sensors, used for a variety of scientific measurements, and without suitable decoding equipment these signals are meaningless – the same is true of satellites used for navigation purposes. Also, most of the communications and television satellites, both for relay and broadcasting, operate at frequencies well removed from the coverage of most scanners.

ORBITING TELEPHONE SATELLITES

With the signals from low-earth satellites having the capability of being quite strong, a natural use for these is for personal telephone use in areas not served by a land-based cellular system. The Iridium system is just one of a number of earth-orbiting systems for global telephone service. This uses 66 satellites forming a cross-linked grid above the Earth, orbiting at 780 km (485 miles) high. They're close enough to receive the signals of a handheld device, and act like cellular base stations in the sky where wireless signals can move overhead instead of through ground-based cells. The low-earth orbit (LEO) allows Iridium phones to be much smaller than those needed for other satellites – small enough to fit in your hand. The satellites also keep track of the users' telephone location anywhere on the globe. An Iridium handset works both as a normal cellphone in areas where a compatible cellular service exists, and as a satellite telephone. As a mobile cellular phone, it seeks out available service from existing land-based networks, and operates the same as cellular systems now in existence, but where cellular service is not available, the Iridium user can switch the phone to satellite operation. The call is then relayed from satellite to satellite until it reaches its destination, either through a local Iridium gateway and the public switched telephone network, or directly to a receiving Iridium phone.

FREQUENCIES

A band of frequencies in L-band, between 1616.0 and 1626.5 MHz, is used as the link between the satellite and Iridium handsets. The Ka-band (19.4–19.6 GHz for downlinks and 29.1–29.3 GHz for uplinks) serves as the link between the satellite and the gateways and earth terminals. The system uses a combination of frequency division multiple access (FDMA) and time division multiple access (TDMA) signals, so although you may be able to receive the digital signal on your scanner, you won't be able to demodulate it using just FM or AM on your scanner – you will need a sophisticated digital decoder.

AMATEUR SATELLITES

Amateur satellite transmissions are among some of the easiest to receive as the satellites are designed to transmit on frequencies that are easily picked up by unsophisticated equipment. Bear in mind that the low-earth orbit satellites, like non-geostationary weather, can only be received for a few minutes at a time as they pass overhead. Occasionally their orbits take them well away from the UK and, at such times, it might not be possible to receive transmissions at all. If possible, use a set of crossed dipoles, or if you're really keen then a yagi aerial that's automatically steerable with a rotator in azimuth and elevation. The way communications take place using these communications satellites is that an amateur transmits up to the satellite on an uplink frequency, the satellite then retransmits the signal back on a different, downlink, frequency. In this way it is quite easy to span large distances using VHF and UHF: communications between Europe and the Americas are quite normal on the elliptic-orbiting satellites, and throughout Europe on the low-earth orbiting ones. This method of retransmitting the signal is known as transponding, which can be either analogue or digital.

FADING SIGNALS?

Remembering the comments in Chapter 4 about aerials and polarisation, one problem in the reception of an orbiting satellites transmissions is that as the satellite moves, its aerial effectively changes polarity in relation to the aerial of the ground station, causing the received signal to, apparently, fade away and then come back again, every few minutes. This can be overcome by using a crossed dipole aerial. Movement of the satellite also causes an effect, known as Doppler shift, which slightly alters the received frequency of the radio signal, higher in frequency as it approaches you and lower in frequency as it goes away. This means a scanner must usually be tuned a few kHz above and then a few kHz below the centre frequency to track the shifting signal. On some scanners with small frequency step controls, this presents no great problem as, fortunately, the manual tuning

Table 8.1 Amateur satellites – analogue transponder downlinks

	Downlink	Beacons
RS-10	29.360–29.400	29.357/29.403
	145.860–145.900	145.857/145.903
RS-11	29.410–29.450	29.403/29.407/29.453
	145.910–145.950	145.907/145.953
RS-12	29.410–29.450	29.408/29.454
	145.910–145.950	145.912/145.958
RS-13	29.460–29.500	29.458/29.504
	145.960–146.000	145.862/145.908
RS-15	29.354–29.394	29.353/29.399
Oscar 10 (Fuji)	145.825–145.975	145.810
Oscar-20 (Fuji)	435.800–345.900	435.795
Oscar-29 (Fuji)	435.800–435.900	435.795

Table 8.2 Amateur satellites – digital transponder downlinks

		Downlink(s)	Data format
Amsat	Oscar 16	437.025	1200 bit/s PSK AX25
		437.050	
		2401.100	
Dove	Oscar 17	145.825	Digitised voice
		2401.220	1200 bits/s AFSK AX25
Webersat	Oscar 18	437.075	1200 bits/s PSK AX25
		437.100	
Lusat	Oscar 19	437.125	1200 bits/s PSK AX25
		437.150	
UOSAT	Oscar 22	435.100	9600 bits/s FSK FM
Kitsat	Oscar 23	435.175	9600 bits/s FSK FM
Kitsat	Oscar 25	436.500	9600 bits/s FSK FM
Itamsat	Oscar 26	435.870	1200 bits/s PSK
Fuji	Oscar 29	435.910	1200 bits/s PSK

Table 8.3 Phase 3D amateur satellite VHF/UHF downlinks

Band	Analogue	Digital
10m	29.330	
2m	145.805–145.955	145.955–145.990
70cm	435.475–435.725	435.900–436.200
13cm	2400.225–2400.475	2400.650–2400.950

control can be used to track the signal, but the inclusion of automatic frequency control (AFC) on suitably equipped scanners can be very helpful.

Tables 8.1, 8.2 and 8.3 list amateur satellites, together with allocated frequencies for the transponder downlink frequencies and the beacons. The RS satellites sometimes have an automatic 'robot' operating on the beacon frequencies. All of the satellites are standard orbiting types apart from Oscar 10, and the Phase 3D satellite (which is yet to be launched at the time of writing) both of which operate in a highly elliptical orbit meaning that they may remain in range for several hours. The RS series is Russian-built while some others have been made by the voluntary organisation, AMSAT. The frequencies of most interest to scanner users are the downlink ones, but it should be noted that often some, if not all, of the satellites are in orbits that are out of UK range, and satellites are occa-

Table 8.4 Weather satellites

Satellite	Frequency
NOAA-12	137.500
NOAA-14	137.620
NOAA-15	137.500
Meteor 3-5	137.850
Okean-4	137.400 (occasional use)
Meteosat-7	1691.000
Meteosat-4	1694.500
Goes-8	1691.000 (Western horizon)

Table 8.5 Miscellaneous satellites

Satellite	Frequency	Details
NASA shuttles	259.700	AM voice
	270.000	AM voice
	296.800	AM voice
Mir (Russia)	142.400	FM voice
	143.625	FM voice
	166.140	Robot/beacon
Soyuz supply modules	121.750	FM voice
Navigation beacons	149.000–150.050	
Cicada	399.000–400.050	Transit

sionally switched off for periods, e.g. to allow for battery charging from their solar panels. The use of a suitable satellite prediction program with up-to-date Keplers for these satellites will tell you exactly when they will be in range of your location.

OTHER SATELLITES

A look at the frequency allocations in Tables 6.1 and 6.2 shows that several bands are allocated for space and satellite operation. Many of these bands have little, if any, activity and in recent years as technology has progressed, space communications have tended to move to higher frequencies – usually of several thousand megahertz. Even so, there is occasionally voice traffic in some of the VHF bands and a list of typical users is given in Table 8.5. Do note, though, that they might not always carry transmissions. For instance two frequencies are shown for the NASA space shuttle but on any one flight this band might never be used. Keen space communications fans know that this side of the hobby often means much patience. If at first you hear nothing, try, try and try again. In the two very narrow navigation satellite bands shown in Table 8.5 it will occasionally be possible to hear either the Russian Cicada system or the USA's Transit service. In the UK reception of Cicada signal transmissions is usually possible several times a day – they are AM signals sounding like fast Morse code.

MILITARY SATCOMS

Most military communications satellites are geostationary and are positioned around 35,000 kilometres out from the equator. Their orbit is synchronised with the Earth's rotation so from the ground they always appear to be in the same position. Their relatively low power output and the distance means their signals are fairly weak by the time they reach us. Ideally a small dipole or ground plane aerial cut for about 270 MHz will probably give better results than a discone (a masthead preamplifier does wonders but most casual listeners probably do not want to go to those lengths). If you want to make up a small ground plane aerial then the active element should be about 260mm long. If you use a steerable log periodic then you should get quite good results. Typical of the sort of satellites that can be heard are the American FleetSatcom series which provide global communications for the US navy. These satellites are transponders which means that their output is on a frequency related to the input frequency (which we are unlikely to hear anyway). Most use FM, although SSB does sometimes appear. Other modes include data, radioteletype and fax. Four of these satellites are positioned around the globe at 25 degrees and 100 degrees west, and 75 degrees and 172 degrees east (all level with the equator). In Europe, FleetSatcom West at 23 degrees longitude can be heard, and I have heard claims that with a suitable aerial it is also possible to hear the Indian Ocean (75 degrees east) satellite as well. The FM used has wider deviation than you will find on normal commercial bands – typically it seems to be around 25 kHz. For best reception you may need to switch your scanner to the WFM mode but unfortunately most scanners are not as sensitive in this mode.

WHAT WILL YOU HEAR?

The easiest transmissions to tune into are the FM voice channels. These often consist of messages being passed from ships or overseas bases back to the United States. There are also phone-patch transmissions between forces and their families on some channels. The digital/data transmissions do not appear to follow the usual commercial formats and one can assume that these are secure messages of strategic importance which have been encoded in some way. I have heard the voice channels being switched to fax transmission and assume that these are normal group 3 fax transmissions, although my own station is only equipped for radio-style fax which is not compatible and so I cannot be absolutely sure.

WHERE TO TUNE

Military satellite transmissions will be heard between 225 and 400 MHz. Possibly the easiest voice channel to hear is Channel X-Ray on FleetSat-

Table 8.6 Military satcoms

User	Frequency
LeaSat (US Navy)	2.850–43.900
FleetSatcom (US navy)	43.960–44.100
Marisat	48.800–49.400
LeaSat (US Air Force)	49.350–249.850
FleetSatcom (US Navy)	260.775–268.350
FM voice traffic has also been heard on the following frequencies:	
244.095, 249.550, 261.500, 261.650, 261.675, 261.950, 262.050, 262.100, 262.225 262.300, 262.475, 263.625, 269.850 & 269.950 MHz.	

com West on 261.675 MHz. This channel is used extensively for phone patches and is one channel which can often be received on nothing more than a telescopic aerial if you have a sensitive scanner. Bands where you should find signals are listed in Table 8.6

9 Scanner and accessories review

A LOOK AT THE EQUIPMENT AVAILABLE IN BRITAIN

So, which scanner should you buy? This chapter looks at the equipment which is on offer from British dealers as well as some earlier models that are still found on the secondhand market. The comments which accompany some models are those of Peter Rouse, Chris Lorek and my own and are based either on measured technical results, on personal experience with the scanner, or general impressions gained from friends and trade sources. Although we have each owned, used and reviewed a great many scanners the comments should not be interpreted as a recommendation for any particular model.

BUYING GUIDE

If you've read up to now, you may already have an idea of the type of scanner you'd like. Invariably, most newcomers will say they want a scanner that covers everything. But let's step back a minute, as this may not necessarily be the best for you. A 'do-everything' scanner will naturally have a large number of operating functions, together with a manual of a large number of pages – one such handheld I've used has a 100-plus page manual. An experienced scanner user will eventually get to grasps with this, but a raw beginner will inevitably find it rather confusing and possibly bewildering. I'm often asked "What's the best scanner to buy?". That's like asking a car enthusiast "What's the best car to buy?". The answer depends on what you want to do with it! There's no point in buying a Ferrari if you just want to use it once a week to go shopping. Likewise, there's no point in paying a lot of money for a scanner which has many features that you won't use, and the inclusion of which could initially be offputting. However, you may have already passed the introductory stage, maybe with a secondhand model or one of the cheap high-street type scanners with limited functions, perhaps having the incorrect 5 kHz rather than 12.5 kHz VHF channel steps – the latter of which you probably wouldn't have bought if you had read and heeded the comments on this in earlier chapters!.

Beginner's scanner

Let's say you're starting out for the first time, and you're looking for a good do-everything scanner at a keen price. The answer to this is naturally very wide, because it really does depend on what your listening interests are. If they extend beyond VHF and UHF, which means HF (i.e. short wave) then I really would recommend an additional HF receiver, and not a wide range scanner which, at least in the lower cost types, give rather marginal performance on HF. Even something like a Matsui or Samsung World Band portable costing less than £100 will, in my mind, be money better spent than a further £100 for additional HF coverage on a scanner.

If you want continuous coverage, rather than banded coverage (i.e. frequency bands with 'gaps' in between) and mode-limited scanner (i.e. AM only on the VHF airband) why not look out for a secondhand offering from AOR, Icom or Yupiteru, the actual type being something to suit your budget and listening needs. Many specialised radio and scanner dealers (not those you'll usually find in the high street – instead look at adverts in magazines such as *Short Wave Magazine*, *Radio Active*, *Radio Today* and *Practical Wireless*) have a constantly changing secondhand stock, and buying from a dealer gives you the benefit of good advice (they want you to return!), as well as a guarantee.

It may seem an obvious statement, but there's little use in looking around for a receiver with the widest coverage possible and plenty of modes if you're only interested in say, the VHF and UHF airband ranges together with ground support frequencies ranges, and you've no interest whatsoever in HF, or the 900 MHz range to listen to analogue cellphones (which you're not allowed to listen to in the UK, and which in any case are being phased out over the forthcoming years in favour of digital GSM). But then, the 1000–2000 MHz range could become more and more interesting in the near future, especially if you're into advanced interests such as telemetry. Decide what your current interests are, and if you're just starting out I'd advise against spending a fortune on the latest hyper-expensive receiver with its equally hyper-complicated controls and buttons.

Frequency ranges and scanning steps

Make sure you buy a receiver that suits your listening interests. For example, many budget scanners offer airband coverage on AM in their descriptions, but they don't cover the UHF military airband range. Others do cover that range, but some can't be switched from FM to AM on bands aside from 108–137 MHz. If you're interested in terrestrial narrowband FM reception in the UK, most services operate on 12.5 kHz steps, so ensure your scanner can accommodate this. Some scanners only allow 5 kHz, 10 kHz, 15 kHz or 25 kHz steps, and although 5 kHz steps will usually bring you 'near enough' you'll find it takes a two and a half times longer to search across a given range in the inappropriate 5 kHz steps rather than in 12.5 kHz increments. Some services, such as 'eye in the sky' traffic reporter links operate with a 6.25 kHz offset so this step could also be useful. You might also consider looking for 8.33 kHz steps for the ultimate in 'future proofing' for VHF airband listening in Europe, although scanners with this are limited at the moment

How much do you want to pay?

In general, although there are some exceptions, the more you pay for a receiver the more features you're likely to get as well as hopefully a better technical performance. If you buy a budget handheld and connect this to a rooftop antenna, particularly an amplified type, don't be surprised to find it falls over with breakthrough from unwanted strong signals on other frequencies when you're trying to listen to a wanted signal. A higher price usually gets you a higher number of available memory channels, several search banks, auto-storage of active frequencies, a switchable attenuator (very useful in busy radio locations to reduce breakthrough), and maybe multi-mode reception to include SSB (Single Sideband, LSB and USB) and CW (Morse code). Few VHF/UHF commercial services use these modes, although if you're interested in listening to amateur radio DX (long distance) stations and contests, it can open up a specialised new world of listening.

HF coverage

Many upmarket receivers offer extended coverage to include the HF (High Frequency) range, i.e. 3–30 MHz and maybe even lower frequencies, and SSB reception is useful here for utility station monitoring. But don't expect to hear much on a set-top antenna or a discone on HF – you'll need a length of wire instead, preferably mounted outdoors and well in the clear. The usual adage here is 'the longer the length of wire the better', but beware as many of the lower priced wideband receivers – I'm talking of below £500 to £1000 here – won't give the performance on HF that you'll get with a similarly priced dedicated HF-only receiver. In other words, connect a good outdoor purpose-designed HF antenna, and you'll often overload the receiver with unwanted off-frequency strong signals to the detriment of what you're actually trying to listen to. If your primary interest is HF, i.e. short wave utility, amateur, and broadcast stations, then spend most of your available budget on a dedicated HF receiver and somewhat less on a further receiver to cover VHF and UHF.

Portable or base

A handheld portable scanner is very useful in that it can double for use at home or outdoors, and will often cost less than a base receiver having similar frequency coverage. A handheld will invariably have a set-top BNC antenna connector so that you can, if you wish, use the receiver at home or out mobile with an external antenna connected in place of the set-top helical. Base scanners are, however, usually easier to operate as there's more room available on the front panel for additional buttons and controls, together with a larger frequency and channel display, and often, but not always in the case of budget models, give better technical performance than a handheld in terms of their ability to receive weaker signals and, more importantly, reject unwanted signals.

Many readers use a handheld scanner for general listening, using this in the car as well as in the home, but a common limitation of using a handheld scanner in a car, when travelling at speed, is usually the low available audio output. Even if an extension speaker is plugged in, you may find there just isn't enough. But here's an idea. Most cars have some form of in-car entertainment, usually a radio/cassette player. A readily available accessory is a portable CD/cassette adapter, which allows you to play a portable CD player through your car's existing radio/cassette system. Using one of these adapters, with the earphone input lead connected instead to your handheld scanner's audio output socket, gives you plenty of audio – even with front/rear fading if your system has this!

Banded or wideband?

Many scanners are what's described as 'banded', i.e. they operate across a given number of frequency ranges rather than having a continuous, i.e. wideband, coverage. But many banded scanners are quasi-wideband in disguise, for example a typical high-street type scanner can be described as covering 68–88 MHz, 108–137 MHz, 137–144 MHz, 144–148 MHz, 148–174 MHz, 380–450 MHz, 450–470 MHz and 470–512 MHz, yet these bands do indeed merge to form one range with just a gap in the 88–108 MHz range. If you're buying a set from the US, possibly whilst visiting there, the low band coverage on US market scanners is usually 29–54

MHz rather than 68–88 MHz as found on European market banded scanners.

The frequency allocations elsewhere in this book give a comprehensive view on what goes on where, however if you're looking at frequency ranges provided on a typical high street scanner, it does sound a lot better as a marketing statement to offer three bands between 137–174 MHz, even though they are all FM with 5 kHz channel spacing and that they provide continuous up/down frequency switching between them. But some gaps do exist, and I hope the brief resumé below will be of use to readers considering one of these types.

68–88 MHz is used by a number of services, mainly private mobile radio but also some government bodies such as the fire and rescue service, together with amateur radio use in the 70.0–70.5 MHz range in the UK. Below 68 MHz however are a number of users, such as amateurs in the 50–52 MHz range, and cordless services such as low-power walkie-talkies, cordless phones and intercoms around 47 MHz and 49 MHz. The rest is generally military and telemetry, using modes other than those normally available on such scanner receiver systems.

87.5–108 MHz is used for wideband FM broadcast radio, of minor interest in a scanner unless of course you also want to listen to this in poor audio quality on a relatively expensive receiver.

108–137 MHz is used around the world for civil airband communication on AM, and is commonly called VHF airband. Some scanners, particularly those intended for US markets where AM is not used on other (non-aircraft) bands, have this range enabled with AM-only reception.

137–174 MHz is commonly available on virtually every scanner on the market, although some only allow FM reception here. But in the UK, not all services use FM, some use AM, so if your scanner doesn't have a switchable mode facility here, you'll occasionally find some rather distorted and unreadable signals in this range (as well as on the 68–88 MHz range). Likewise, many cheaper scanners only allow 5 kHz frequency steps in this range, whereas in the UK we use 12.5 kHz and 25 kHz steps. Although in some cases you won't be able to accurately tune to the exact frequency in use, the naturally wide IF filters in these scanners often allow adequate reception. What *is* a limitation though is that the overall search speed is reduced, due to the unnecessarily small frequency steps.

Just above 174 MHz you'll find radio microphones, and higher still is the Band III range (extending up to 225 MHz). This is used by a number of services, particularly public transport such as railways and buses/coaches.

The upper section is intended for future digital modes such as TETRA (Trans-European Trunked Radio) which is planned to be used by people such as the emergency services. Part of this band is also set aside for Digital Audio Broadcasting (DAB), which is currently in 'trial' mode from a couple of sites in the UK.

The frequency spectrum *225–400 MHz* is virtually exclusively used for military airband communications, and is commonly called UHF airband. This also uses AM but typically with 50 kHz minimum channel spacing. If you're interested in military airband monitoring, ensure this range is covered on your scanner, and that you can receive AM signals on it – many scanners with airband coverage claimed only cover VHF airband.

400–406 MHz is used for satellite communication, but *406–470 MHz* is used by a very large number of services in the UK. These range from low-power walkie-talkies and alarms, to countrywide government communi-cation users such as the police. You can usually dismiss the range from about 470 MHz upwards on a scanner, as this spectrum, up to 854 MHz, is used for TV broadcasting. Above 854 MHz and up to 950 MHz are serv-ices such cellular phones.

I hope the above will help potential scanner buyers in deciding whether the extra £100 or so extra is worthwhile spending to get a wideband all-coverage scanner or not

Wideband scanners

If you don't want to miss a thing, these are the types to go for, and in a number of cases you may find you're not paying a premium. The small Icom IC-R2 for example is a compact wideband model but with a price tag actually less than a number of banded scanners. What you'll normally find however is that extra facilities, such a band-scope, alpha-tagging of memory channels, and the inclusion of SSB, increases the price accord-ingly. If you're choosing a sophisticated model as your first set, ensure you're happy in knowing how to use it, preferably in the shop with a 'hands-on' test, before parting with your money.

Dedicated airband scanners

Although the majority of scanners cover the civil airband, many of them offer performance which is something of a compromise. Airband trans-missions are AM mode and the ideal circuitry for AM differs to that for FM. Although the majority of dual or multi-mode scanners offer adequate performance on airband, they rarely achieve the same level of performance as dedicated airband scanners such as the Sony, WIN or Signal models where the RF, IF and AGC circuits are optimised for the band and mode. The IF bandwidth particularly needs to be wide enough to accommodate offset carriers which are sometimes encountered on the civil airband range.

Where to buy from

The most important advice is to buy from a dealer who will have proper facilities to repair any equipment he sells you. If your new scanner is going to go wrong in the first few years of use it will statistically do so in the first few weeks you own it, and there can be nothing more infuriating than waiting for weeks or even months for it to be repaired. If you buy a scanner from a dealer who specialises in this kind of equipment (most amateur radio equipment shops do have facilities) then repair should be fairly fast. On the other hand if you buy from the high street shop that sells a few TVs, radios and household appliances they are unlikely to have the kind of sophisticated equipment nor the experience to repair or realign sophisticated VHF/UHF equipment. Never mind what the salesman says, it is a specialised area of servicing. With a specialised dealer you will also get proper advice on choosing a scanner. Salesmen who work in the majority of amateur radio type shops are usually enthusiasts and know their products well. On the other hand I could fill a book with some of the fantastic claims and howlers I have heard pour from the mouths of shop assistants selling scanners in Hi-Fi/TV shops.

Buying used equipment

Used scanners are commonly available from specialised radio dealers, these often having been traded in as a customer upgrades to a more sophisticated model. Buying a secondhand scanner from such a dealer will usually give you the best assurance of getting what you want as well as a 3-month guarantee. Secondhand equipment is also advertised in the reader's adverts sections of magazines devoted to hobby radio, as well as sometimes in local free sales papers. When buying a used scanner from an individual rather than a dealer, if at all possible take an experienced scanner user with you. The first thing to check is the frequency coverage and, if it is important to your choice of listening, whether or not the mode is selectable on all bands. Also take a look at its general appearance – if it has a number of scratches or other damage then it's obviously seen a rough time, however most current scanners stand up to this well and will often operate perfectly. But watch out for any evidence of internal tampering, such as chewed-up screw heads on the case. It may have had the attention of a 'screwdriver expert' inside, possibly to the detriment of the

Secondhand scanners are readily available from dealers.

set's performance. The worst offenders are often those people with a little knowledge of radio circuitry and so be doubly cautious if the seller seems to be well versed in technology. Obviously you should ask for a demonstration of the scanner and don't be afraid to ask if the owner has had any problems with it or had it repaired.

Prices

These constantly change as Far-Eastern manufacturing technology changes as well as currency fluctuations. The best guide is to consult a recent copy of a dedicated radio magazine, where you'll often find dealers adverting such equipment. Some also have a couple of pages purely of dealers' lists of secondhand equipment, and the reader's ads will undoubtedly have several offers you might be tempted with.

The following section on actual equipment has been updated to take account of new scanners available, and the technical performance figures, where given below, are real measurements of a typical and representative sample of the scanner model in each case. All the results are from measurements made in exactly the same way, and are independent of any manufacturer's 'claims' or 'specifications', which due to the different methods of each manufacturer's specifications can often give a meaningless comparison! For the technically minded, the results given here are measured as:

Sensitivity Input signal level in μV pd giving 12dB SINAD.

Adjacent channel selectivity Increase in level of interfering signal, modulated with 400 Hz at 1.5 kHz deviation, above 12dB SINAD reference level to cause 6dB degradation in 12dB on-channel signal.

Blocking As adjacent channel selectivity.

Intermodulation rejection Increase over 12dB SINAD level of two interfering signals giving identical 12dB SINAD 3rd order inter-modulation product (i.e., the unwanted on-channel signal produced from two off-channel signals). All measurements, except sensitivity where stated, were taken on 145 MHz NFM to ensure uniformity (apart from airband-only sets where 125 MHz AM was used).

Alinco DJ-X1D

Type:	Handheld
Coverage:	500 kHz 1300 MHz continuous
Modes:	AM, FM, Wide FM
Sensitivity:	20 MHz 0.37μV AM, 0.20μV FM 145 MHz 0.16μV AM, 0.13μV FM 435 MHz 0.18μV AM, 0.12μV FM 934 MHz 0.20 MHz 0.20μV FM
Adjacent channel:	12.5 kHz 18.9dB 25 kHz 40.9dB
Blocking:	100 kHz 40.9dB 1 MHz 80.6dB 10 MHz 87.1db
Intermodulation:	25/50 kHz 24.0dB 50/100 kHz 27.9dB

A wideband scanner, giving plenty of listening scope in a slightly chunky but still compact handheld-sized case. Some European versions of this model come supplied with coverage of the amateur bands only, all other frequency ranges being locked out unless you tap in the right numbers (which the UK distributors supply on an information sheet with the set), so beware if you're buying from abroad. The D suffix of the DJ-X1D is supposed to mean it's an improved version of the DJ-X1, better suited to handling strong signals. It does give good performance from out-of-band signals, but connect an outside aerial and you'll most likely have a lot of problems from signals up to a few channels away from the one you're tuned to.

Alinco DJ-X10

Type:	Handheld
Coverage:	500 kHz 2000 MHz continuous
Modes:	AM, FM, Wide FM, USB, LSB, CW
Channels:	1200
Sensitivity:	20 MHz 0.13µV SSB, 0.23µV AM, 0.15µV FM 145 MHz 0.18µV SSB, 0.28µV AM, 0.18µV FM 435 MHz 0.32µV SSB, 0.28µV FM 950 MHz 0.27µV FM
Adjacent channel:	12.5 kHz 24.9dB 25 kHz 47.7dB
Blocking:	100 kHz 61.1dB 1 MHz 78.8dB
Intermodulation:	25/50 kHz 61.8dB 50/100 kHz 59.4dB

A 'go anywhere on any frequency and any mode' scanner in a slim case. It's neat, easy to use, and gives good performance on air. The scanner has both beginner and expert operating modes as well as auto-mode and auto-step functions, which make it useful for even the beginner. There are plenty of useful memory scanning facilities, also a facility to alpha-tag memory channels plus a band-scope display. There's an auto-store facility, but this repeatedly stores channels already found until the memory bank is filled up – not a lot of use. The inclusion of SSB is useful for HF listening, although it's naturally not up to the performance of a purpose-designed HF receiver.

AOR AR-1500EX

Type:	Handheld
Coverage:	500 MHz 1300 MHz continuous
Modes:	AM, FM, SSB with built-in BFO
Channels:	1000
Sensitivity:	20 MHz 0.18µV 0.12µV FM 145 MHz 0.22µV AM 0.13µV FM 435 MHz 0.45µV AM 0.38µV FM 934 MHz 0.57µV FM
Adjacent channel:	12.5 kHz 34.0dB 25 kHz 53.5dB
Blocking:	100 kHz 48.0dB 1 MHz 75.0dB 10 MHz 97.0dB
Intermodulation:	25/50 kHz 45.0dB 50/100 kHz 48.0dB

This wideband handheld scanner sells at only a little more than AOR's similar, but AM/FM only, AR-2000 scanner, yet it gains a lot from its switchable Beat Frequency Oscillator (BFO). This lets you use the set to far greater advantage on HF, for example allowing reception of HF airband (used when craft are over the oceans, out of VHF range), utility stations, and radio amateurs. The scanner can't be classed as a purpose-designed SSB receiver, but it's certainly OK for occasional listening around on this mode. You might even be able to tune into 6m, 4m, 2m, 70cm and 23cm SSB stations during contests which very few other scanners at this price will let you do.

AOR AR-2000

Type:	Handheld
Coverage:	500 kHz 1300 MHz continuous
Modes:	AM, FM, Wide FM
Channels:	1000

This set is essentially identical to the AR-1500 but without the BFO facility. Look out for this set as a good secondhand buy for wideband AM/FM listening.

AOR AR-2002

Type: Base/mobile
Coverage: 25–550 MHz, 800–1300 MHz
Modes: AM, FM, Wide FM
Channels: 20

This early model from AOR looks broadly similar in styling to the superb but quite different AR-3000A. The AR-2002 is reputed to give good performances on-air, as well as being easy to use. A very wide band coverage will let you listen to plenty of things, but you only have 20 memories available to store all those interesting frequencies in. It does, however, have an RS-232 remote control connector, which allows you to use the power of your PC for this. If you're after something secondhand to use at home and don't mind the limited built-in memories, you could get a good bargain.

AOR AR-2800

Type: Base/mobile
Coverage: 500 kHz 600 MHz, 800 MHz 1300 MHz
Modes: AM, FM, Wide FM, SSB
Channels: 1000
Sensitivity: 20 MHz 0.57µV AM 145 MHz 0.31µV AM, 0.20µV
                  FM 435 MHz 0.28µV FM 934 MHz 0.29µV FM
Adjacent channel: 12.5 kHz 33.0dB 25 kHz 33.0dB
Blocking: 100 kHz 56.5dB 1 MHz 75.5dB 10 MHz 97.0dB

Like the AR-1500 handheld, it packs in a lot of frequency coverage at a reasonable price, and has a switchable BFO so you can tune into SSB signals on HF and VHF/UHF bands. A nice extra touch is a vertical bargraph made up of LEDs to give a relative display of the received signal level. The very wide band coverage, with just a gap in between (which is used for TV broadcasting in the UK) should let you tune into lots of signals, the sensible number of 1000 channels being more than enough to suit most user's needs in terms of frequency storage. Watch out though, it isn't a purpose-made HF SSB receiver, it will 'curl up' if you put a well-sited outdoor aerial on it, although you can switch in an internal attenuator to reduce the effects of this. For searching around on VHF/UHF, either AM or FM, an AF-scan toggle switch is hidden at the back of the case.

AOR AR-3000A

Type:	Base/mobile
Coverage:	100 kHz–2036 MHz
Modes:	AM, FM, Wide FM, CW, LSB, SSB
Channels:	400
Sensitivity:	20 MHz 0.12µV SSB 0.34µV AM 0.16µV FM
	145 MHz 0.17µV SSB 0.48µV AM 0.24µV FM
	435 MHz 0.18µV SSB 0.51µV AM 0.25µV FM
	934 MHz 0.26µV FM
Adjacent channel:	12.5 kHz 42.0dB 25 kHz 52.5dB
Blocking:	100 kHz 67.0dB 1 MHz 79.0dB 10 MHz 94.5dB
Intermodulation:	25/50 kHz 41.5dB 50/100 kHz 41.0dB

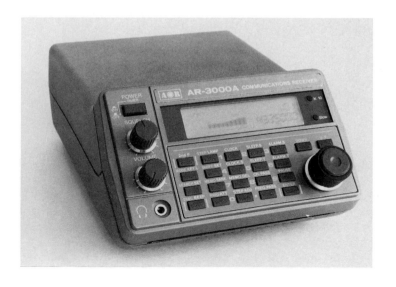

If you think of what you'd like in a mobile or base scanner and then make a wish list', this one's probably rather a lot of them. With coverage up to 2036 MHz, you could even have a go at tuning in some of the geostationary communications satellites, and at the other end of the spectrum, short wave broadcast, utility, amateur, and HF airband and marine signals. Add a PC running 'Searchlight' software available from AOR, and you have a very powerful listening station. It's little wonder the UK government are reputed to have bought a large number of these for themselves. It isn't cheap, but it's worth every penny – secondhand models are very sought after.

AOR AR-5000

Type:	Base
Coverage:	10 kHz 2600 MHz
Modes:	AM, FM, Wide FM, CW, LSB, SSB
Channels:	1000
Sensitivity:	20 MHz 0.23µV SSB 0.81µV AM 0.43µV FM
	145 MHz 0.17µV SSB 0.46µV AM 0.24µV FM
	435 MHz 0.19µV SSB 0.26µV FM 950 MHz 0.30µV FM
Adjacent channel:	12.5 kHz 50.9dB 25 kHz 54.2dB
Blocking:	100 kHz 75.4dB 1 MHz 92.6dB 10 MHz 95.2dB
Intermodulation:	25/50 kHz 76.0dB

About the ultimate in base scanners, this one's got the lot. There's also an AR5000+3 model with added synchronous AM, Automatic Frequency Control(AFC) and a noise blanker. A staggeringly wide frequency range, selectable bandwidths of 3, 6, 15, 30, 110 and 220 kHz and even the facility of adding an optional 500 Hz or 1 kHz filter for CW or data. It gives excellent on-air performance with very good rejection of unwanted signals. A remote control port lets you couple a PC up to this superb receiver to give an extremely capable and very powerful monitoring tool.

AOR AR-8000

Type:	Handheld
Coverage:	500 kHz 1900 MHz continuous
Modes:	AM, FM, Wide FM, USB, LSB, CW
Channels:	1000
Sensitivity:	20 MHz 0.22µV SSB, 0.33µV AM, 145 MHz 0.19µV SSB, 0.28µV FM, 435 MHz 0.36µV SSB, 0.32µV FM, 950 MHz 0.32µV FM, 1600 MHz 2.89µV FM
Adjacent channel:	12.5 kHz 38.3dB, 25 kHz 47.5dB
Blocking:	100 kHz 60.8dB 1 MHz 68.9dB
Intermodulation:	25/50 kHz 73.8dB 50/ 100 kHz 62.6dB

Plenty of operating modes, including a new user mode for simple operation which you can switch to expert as you progress. An auto-mode facility in band segments is very useful, the scanner changing mode as needed when you tune around, as well as an alphanumeric text display giving helpful information while you're programming, and a band-scope. An auto-store facility is fitted which works well, and a remote control facility. You can password protect the upper 500 memory channels to save prying eyes, although a hard microprocessor reset disables this yet retains the memories should you forget your four-digit lock code.

AOR AR-8200

Type:	Handheld
Coverage:	530 kHz 2040 MHz continuous
Modes:	AM, FM, Wide FM, USB, LSB, CW
Channels:	1000

Sensitivity:	20 MHz 0.13µV SSB, 0.53µV AM, 145 MHz 0.13µV SSB, 0.18µV FM, 435 MHz 0.22µV FM, 800 MHz 0.47µV FM, 1700 MHz 0.61µV FM
Adjacent channel:	12.5 kHz 25.7dB, 25 kHz 44.4dB
Blocking:	100 kHz 65.3dB, 1 MHz 71.3dB, 10 MHz 86.1dB
Intermodulation:	25/50 kHz 53.7dB, 50/100 kHz 52.7dB

Packed to bursting with 'bells and whistles', this one's probably the most feature-filled handheld scanner around. A large dot-matrix LCD gives a text display for memory alpha-tagging as well as a band-scope. A useful facility of the latter is a 'peak hold' where you can leave the set scanning and return later to see what activity there's been. A vast number of scanning modes including carrier, speech, level etc., even a remote control port. A detachable medium wave bar aerial is fitted which gives good portable reception in this range. There are a number of small plug-in options available, including an add-on memory unit (4 groups of 1000 channels each), a voice inverter, a CTCSS unit, an audio tone eliminator and even a digital audio recorder. The inclusion of selectable 8.33 kHz channel spacing steps makes this one future-proof for VHF airband.

Bearcat BC-890XLT

Type:	Base
Coverage:	29–54, 108–512 MHz, 806–1300 MHz
Modes:	AM, FM
Channels:	200
Sensitivity:	29 MHz 0.32µV FM 145 MHz 0.34µV FM, 435 MHz 0.55µV FM 934 MHz 0.27µV FM
Adjacent channel:	12.5 kHz 4.8dBdB, 25 kHz 56.4dB
Blocking:	100 kHz 68.3dB, 1 MHz 79.3dB, 10 MHz 86.3dB

A large sized base scanner from Bearcat, offering quite an impressive-looking desktop set. It's packed with handy operating facilities such as an automatic store facility and quick access for scanning your favourite banks of frequencies, which are arranged as 20 banks of 10 channels each. Turbo Scan gives a fast scan rate of around 100 channels per second,

meaning you shouldn't miss very much. The frequency steps can usefully be programmed to either 5 kHz, 12.5 kHz or 25 kHz, you're not stuck with 5 kHz steps on VHF like other scanners which are also designed for the US market.

Bearcat BC-2500XLT

Type: Handheld
Coverage: 25–550, 760–1300 MHz
Modes: AM, FM, Wide FM
Channels: 400

This one's a full-feature model from Bearcat, with 400 channels arranged into 20 banks, and an automatic store to help fill these for you with locally active frequencies. Turbo Scan mode lets you hunt around at almost 100 channels per second, and for manual tuning a rotary knob is fitted. The set automatically switches between AM and FM depending on the sub-band selected (AM for Civil and Military airband plus 25–29 MHz, FM otherwise), which could either be useful or limiting, depending on your needs.

Black Jaguar MkIV

Type: Handheld
Coverage: 28–30 MHz, 60–88
            MHz, 115–178 MHz,
            210–260 MHz,
            410–520 MHz
Modes: AM, FM
Channels: 16

An early handheld scanner, which can be picked up on the secondhand market, although rather heavy and bulky by today's standards.

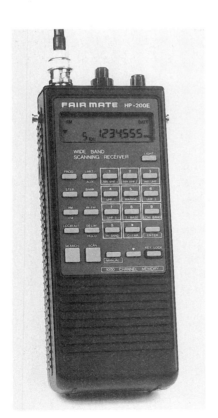

Fairmate HP-2000

Type: Handheld
Coverage: 100 kHz 1300 MHz
Modes: AM, FM, Wide FM
Channels: 1000

Looking remarkably similar to the AR-2000, it also has many of the same facilities, although the lower tuning range has been extended to 100 kHz.

Icom IC-PCR100

Type:	PC controlled
Coverage:	500 kHz 1300 MHz
Modes:	AM, FM, Wide FM
Sensitivity:	20 MHz 0.77μV
	AM 0.32μV FM
	145 MHz 0.55μV
	AM 0.25μV FM
	435 MHz 0.46μV
	AM 0.23μV FM
	1300 MHz 0.35μV
	FM
Adjacent channel:	12.5 kHz 48.6dB 25 kHz 59.3dB
Blocking:	100 kHz 71.9dB 1 MHz 82.2dB 10 MHz 78.4dB
Intermodulation:	25/50 kHz 47.2dB 50/100 kHz 55.9dB

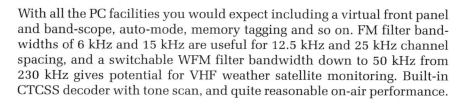

With all the PC facilities you would expect including a virtual front panel and band-scope, auto-mode, memory tagging and so on. FM filter bandwidths of 6 kHz and 15 kHz are useful for 12.5 kHz and 25 kHz channel spacing, and a switchable WFM filter bandwidth down to 50 kHz from 230 kHz gives potential for VHF weather satellite monitoring. Built-in CTCSS decoder with tone scan, and quite reasonable on-air performance.

Icom IC-PCR1000

Type:	PC controlled
Coverage:	500 kHz 1300 MHz
Modes:	AM, FM, Wide FM, USB, LSB, CW

'Big brother' to the IC-PCR100, this adds SSB capabilities together with three different types of virtual front panel display with the supplied Icom software. With the very comprehensive scanning facilities you'd expect, although the band-scope mutes receive audio while it is searching around.

Icom IC-R1

Type:	Handheld
Coverage:	100 kHz 1300 MHz
Modes:	AM, FM, Wide FM
Channels:	100
Sensitivity:	30 MHz 0.34μV AM 0.32μV FM 145 MHz 0.31μV
	AM 0.25μV FM 435 MHz 0.42μV AM 0.27μV FM
	934 MHz 0.38μV FM
Adjacent channel:	12.5 kHz 21.8dB 25 kHz 33.0dB
Blocking:	100 kHz 31.0dB 1 MHz 67.5dB 10 MHz 79.5dB
Intermodulation:	50/100 kHz 24.0dB

Icom's first handheld scanner squeezes in wideband coverage and a number of nice features like switchable steps of 0.5, 5, 8, 9, 10, 12.5, 20, 25 and 50 kHz for tuning increments. Another potentially useful mode is Auto-Memory Write Scan which allows you to set the receiver searching across a band, and it will automatically store the first 19 channels where it finds a signal. Unfortunately, the set suffers from the manufacturer's attempts of trying to cram a lot in, and it also suffers from strong-signal overload from adjacent channels unless an internal crystal filter addition modification has been performed.

Icom IC-R2

Type:	Handheld
Coverage:	500 kHz 1310 MHz
Modes:	AM, FM, Wide FM
Channels:	400

A neat and very portable scanner, lightweight and with the footprint of a credit card, and very reasonably priced. It's powered by two AA batteries so spares are easily carried for an extended listening spell away from home. 50 extra memory channels are fitted as band-edge channels for searching, and a CTCSS tone-scan lets you see which tone is in use on the channel you're monitoring as well as the set using tone squelch to monitor only signals with the correct tone. A cloning facility lets you upload and download channels with another IC-R2 or a PC.

Icom IC-R10

Type:	Handheld
Coverage:	500 kHz 1300 MHz
Modes:	AM, FM, Wide FM, SSB, CW
Channels:	1000
Sensitivity:	20 MHz 0.22µV SSB 0.36µV AM 0.23µV FM
	145 MHz 0.21µV SSB 0.31µV AM 0.18µV FM
	435 MHz 0.38µV SSB 0.34µV FM 950 MHz 0.35µV FM
Adjacent channel:	12.5 kHz 21.9dB 25 kHz 50.6dB
Blocking:	100 kHz 59.4dB 1 MHz 83.9dB 10 MHz 87.8dB
Intermodulation:	25/50 kHz 52.6dB 50/100 kHz 53.1dB

The 'big brother' to the IC-R1 and R2, this one includes SSB receive and a remote port for full remote control from a PC, as well as memory upload/download. A unique facility of being able to listen to one channel while the set automatically searches for the next busy channel speeds listening up remarkably. An 'easy' mode gives you a rapid scan of pre-programmed ranges and there is also an auto-write scan fitted to locate and store new channels for you as well as a band-scope. Reasonable on-air performance although connecting an external aerial could bring problems in busy areas.

Icom IC-R100

Type:	Base/mobile
Coverage:	100 kHz 1800 MHz
Modes:	AM, FM, Wide FM
Channels:	100
Sensitivity:	30 MHz 1.12µV AM 0.51µV FM 145 MHz 0.39µV AM 0.18µV FM 435 MHz 0.58µV AM 0.27µV FM 934 MHz 0.23µV FM
Adjacent channel:	12.5 kHz 42.3dB 25 kHz 62.3dB
Blocking:	100 kHz 75.5dB 1 MHz 91.5dB 10 MHz 105dB
Intermodulation:	50/100 kHz 55.0dB

A quality receiver in a car-radio sized case. Useful facilities such as switchable VHF preamp and Automatic Frequency Control (AFC) helps in weak signal reception of orbiting satellites. The 1800 MHz upper frequency coverage accommodates geostationary satellites as well.

Icom ICR-7100

Type: Base
Coverage: 25 MHz 2000 MHz
Modes: AM, FM, Wide FM, LSB, USB
Channels: 900

This receiver, like its predecessor the ICR-7000, has been the choice of serious VHF/UHF listeners for some time, including many professional users. Its SSB reception capability lets you listen to plenty of extra activity, and the 2000 MHz upper limit tuning (although the specifications are only guaranteed up to 1300MHz) again puts it in the realms of the serious-listening category. Remote computer control facilities are also available via a CI-V port.

Icom ICR-8500

Type:	Base
Coverage:	100 kHz 2000 MHz
Modes:	AM, FM, Wide FM, LSB, USB, CW
Sensitivity:	20 MHz 0.14µV SSB 0.38µV AM 0.18µV FM
	145 MHz 0.17µV SSB 0.45µV AM 0.21µV FM
	435 MHz 0.15µV SSB 0.19µV FM 1800 MHz
	0.43µV FM
Adjacent channel:	12.5 kHz 58.8dB 25 kHz 67.0dB
Blocking:	100 kHz 78.4dB 1 MHz 94.3dB 10 MHz 95.9dB
Intermodulation:	25/50 kHz 75.2dB 50/100 kHz 74.6dB

A worthy and equally powerful successor to the IC-R7000 and 7100 family. More of a serious receiver than a desktop scanner, this model adds HF coverage, an IF shift control and Automatic Peak Filter (APF) being useful here. PC control facilities add to the set's already powerful scanning and monitoring capabilities.

Icom ICR-9000

Type:	Base
Coverage:	100 kHz 2000 MHz
Modes:	AM, FM, Wide FM, SSB, CW, FSK
Channels:	1000

One for the serious listener and a receiver certainly also aimed at the professional user. It's a full-blooded base station VHF/UHF communications receiver more than a scanner, and the 75mm cathode ray tube display is used to good effect as a narrowband monitor to show you what's going on up to 100 kHz either side of your tuned frequency. Icom's CI-V remote control system is available, with professional software also available.

Kenwood RZ-1

Type:	Base/mobile
Coverage:	500 kHz 905 MHz
Modes:	AM, FM, Wide FM
Channels:	100
Sensitivity:	20 MHz 1.7µV AM 145 MHz 5.01µV AM 0.28µV FM 435 MHz 1.09µV FM
Adjacent channel:	12.5 kHz 34.5dB 25 kHz 40.5dB
Intermodulation:	50/100 kHz 64.0dB

This car-radio-sized scanner covers from Long Wave upwards and with its wideband coverage including HF it could make it a different sort of car radio to have. It's a little insensitive on AM with no squelch on this mode, also to listen to FM stereo you'll need an external stereo amplifier.

Netset PRO-44

Type:	Handheld
Coverage:	68–88, 108–137, 137–174, 380–512 MHz (AM)
Modes:	FM, AM on airband
Channels:	50
Sensitivity:	145 MHz 0.44µV 435 MHz 0.70µV
Adjacent channel:	12.5 kHz 11.4dB 25 kHz 69.3dB
Blocking:	100 kHz 61.4dB 1 MHz 85.7dB 10 MHz 86.5dB
Intermodulation:	25/50 kHz 56.3dB 50/100 kHz 56.9dB

It's cheap, it's remarkably similar to the earlier but more expensive Realistic PRO-43 sold by the same chain of retailers, and like its predecessor it's also available in the high street. It isn't designed specifically for UK use – on VHF you're stuck with 5 kHz steps and no AM apart from on the airband section and on UHF you'll hear signals on the image frequency (i.e. not the one you're tuned to) twice as strong as the one you want to listen to – but it's cheap and easily available.

Netset PRO-46

Type: Handheld

Coverage: 68–88, 108–137,
137–174, 406–512,
806–956 MHz

Modes: FM, AM on airband
Channels: 100
Sensitivity: 145 MHz 0.26µV
435 MHz 0.24µV
934 MHz 0.48µV
Adjacent channel: 12.5 kHz 13.3dB
25 kHz 64.4dB
Blocking: 100 kHz 63.2dB
1 MHz 78.6dB
10 MHz 88.9dB
Intermodulation: 25/50 kHz 60.3dB
50/100 kHz
59.1dB

This one's rather similar in terms of
coverage to its smaller brother the Netset
PRO-44, but adds coverage of 806–
956MHz, with small missing segments
corresponding to the cellular frequency
bands used in the US (but not in the UK).
This is a 'dead giveaway' of its intended market, and again you're stuck
with 5 kHz steps on VHF and no AM apart from the airband range. The
poor image rejection here is in the 900 MHz region, where it receives
image signals slightly stronger than the wanted signal. However, it's readily available in the high street, it's reasonably priced, and that is what will
sell it.

Netset PRO-2032

Type: Base/mobile
Coverage: 68–88, 108–137, 137–174, 380–512, 806–96 MHz
Modes: FM, AM on airband
Channels: 200

Another high street scanner, this one's sure to be a popular choice in the
UK due to its wide availability. A fast scanning rate of 25 memories per
second, or 50 frequencies per second in search mode, should mean you
don't miss much while the set's looking around for signals. 5 kHz steps on
VHF together with AM only on airband is a limitation, although the
value-for-money aspect makes up for this.

Nevada MS-1000
Type: Base/mobile
Coverage: 500 MHz 600 MHz, 800 1300 MHz
Modes: AM, FM, Wide FM
Channels: 1000

With similar features to some of the Yupiteru base/mobile scanners, this one's an OEM model from the UK firm of Nevada. The wideband coverage

should make sure you have plenty to listen to, and the UK source may be an advantage in terms of backup.

Optoelectronics Optocom

Type:	PC controlled
Coverage:	25–550, 760–1300 MHz
Modes:	AM, FM, Wide FM
Sensitivity:	25 MHz 0.80µV AM 0.27µV FM 145 MHz 0.59µV AM 0.40µV FM 435 MHz 0.36µV AM 0.23µV FM 1300 MHz 0.78µV FM
Adjacent channel:	12.5 kHz 8.4dB 25 kHz 59.3dB
Blocking:	100 kHz 59.1dB 1 MHz 77.8dB 10 MHz 79.2dB
Intermodulation:	50/100 kHz 57.5dB

The US manufacturers of the Optocom PC-controlled receiver make their control protocol openly available so that third parties can also produce software, and such exists which gives an even more flexible alternative to the supplied software. Used with Trunk Tracker software, which is supplied, the Optocom has the capability of tracking both the Motorola and EDACS (but not MPT1327) trunked radio system, although software for MPT1327 as widely used in Europe may also become available. The set has a built-in store of 28 memory channels as well as front-panel volume and squelch knobs, so after uploading from a PC it can be used as a stand-alone receiver when needed.

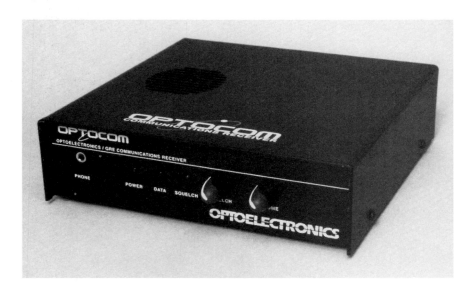

Optoelectronics Scout

Not a scanner as such but a frequency finder. It is a sensitive frequency counter which can hunt out and store active frequencies in use in a local area. Depending upon the output power and aerial of the transmitter, signals with ranges of between a few metres and half a kilometre can be detected. The Scout has a built-in frequency memory to store over 100 active channels– these can be manually cycled through to view the frequencies. A very useful facility is a data port which can connect with suitably equipped scanners, e.g. the AR8000 and 8200, to automatically tune the connected scanner receiver to the detected frequency.

Optoelectronics Xplorer

This is a wideband sweeping receiver in a self-contained portable metal case, with a built-in detector and audio amplifier. Like the Scout it detects local signals, but instead of giving a frequency readout you actually hear the signal it has found. There is a lockout facility to prevent it halting on unwanted strong carriers.

Realistic PRO-25

Type:	Handheld
Coverage:	68–88, 108–174, 406–512, 806–956 MHz
Modes:	AM airband, FM
Channels:	100
Sensitivity:	145 MHz 0.30µV 435 MHz 0.23µV 934 MHz 0.26µV
Adjacent channel:	12.5 kHz 9.6dB 25 kHz 62.7dB
Blocking:	100 kHz 65.6dB 1 MHz 83.4dB 10 MHz 94.9dB
Intermodulation:	25/50 kHz 57.5dB 50/100 kHz 62.1dB

A lightweight portable scanner, although it is restricted to 5 kHz channel steps on VHF and, strangely, 12.5 kHz steps on VHF airband.

Realistic PRO-26

Type:	Handheld
Coverage:	25-1300 MHz continuous
Modes:	AM, FM
Channels:	200
Sensitivity:	145 MHz 0.26µV FM,
	435 MHz 0.47µV FM,
	934 MHz 0.12µV FM
Adjacent channel:	12.5 kHz 0.3dB 25 kHz
	51.1dB
Blocking:	100 kHz 63.5dB 1 MHz
	69.6dB 10 MHz 88.5dB
Intermodulation:	25/50 kHz 55.4dB
	50/100 kHz 56.8dB

This handheld can usefully be switched to either AM or FM throughout its range, and 10 monitor memories in addition to the 200 normal channels are provided for quick storage. A default mode and channel spacing, based on US use, is programmed in which the receiver switches to on each frequency change, although this can be manually changed each time after you've entered the frequency. A triple conversion gives good image rejection, an auto-memory store facility is fitted which works well, together with a fast channel scan rate of around 50 channels a second.

Realistic PRO-27

Type:	Handheld
Coverage:	68–88, 137–174,
	406–512 MHz
Modes:	FM
Channels:	20
Sensitivity:	145 MHz 0.28µV
	435 MHz 0.47µV
Adjacent channel:	12.5 kHz 8.7dB 25 kHz
	59.5dB
Blocking:	100 kHz 60.1dB 1 MHz
	85.9dB 10 MHz 93.0dB
Intermodulation:	25/50 kHz 55.7dB
	50/100 kHz 61.4dB

A low-cost starter, possibly worth looking at if you're not interested in airband coverage. A couple of button pushes can usefully make the scanner search across one of seven pre-stored band ranges. Easy to use but limited to 5 kHz steps on VHF.

Realistic PRO-28

Type:	Handheld
Coverage:	68–88, 137–174, 406–512 MHz
Modes:	FM
Channels:	30
Sensitivity:	145 MHz 0.27µV 435 MHz 0.33µV
Adjacent channel:	12.5 kHz 8.0dB 25 kHz 56.7dB
Blocking:	100 kHz 65.3dB 1 MHz 84.3dB 10 MHz 93.1dB
Intermodulation:	25/50 kHz 52.1dB 50/100 kHz 60.3dB

Another low-cost non-airband starter, with 30 memory channels and 7 pre-stored search ranges although again with 5 kHz steps on VHF.

Realistic PRO-29

Type:	Handheld
Coverage:	68–88, 108–174, 406–512, 806–965 MHz
Modes:	AM airband, FM
Channels:	60
Sensitivity:	145 MHz 0.333µV 435 MHz 0.48µV 950 MHz 0.39µV
Adjacent channel:	12.5 kHz 5.0dB 25 kHz 61.2dB
Blocking:	100 kHz 70.7dB 1 MHz 86.0dB 10 MHz 94.4dB
Intermodulation:	25/50 kHz 54.0dB 50/100 kHz 61.7dB

Yet another starter handheld from the high street, this time with VHF airband included as well as upper UHF. A few extra facilities are included, such as pre-programmable search range and priority channel scan, as well as the facility to enter up to 30 search skip frequencies for the set to ignore on subsequent searches. The receiver has a fixed step size of 5 kHz on VHF.

Realistic PRO-39
Type: Handheld
Coverage: 68–88, 108–137, 137–174, 806–956 MHz
Modes: FM, AM on airband
Channels: 200

A 10-channel monitor bank, which you can use as a scratch pad when scanning, helps you fill the set's memory channels adding to the 200 channels. This one is reasonably popular due to its wide availability, although the lack of switchable AM/FM can cause limitations.

Realistic PRO-41
Type: Handheld
Coverage: 68–88, 137–174, 406–512 MHz
Modes: FM
Channels: 10

Having just 10 channels which you manually program, this is a low-cost scanner that's available at an economic price. It doesn't have a search facility, so you need to know which frequencies you want to listen to before you can listen to anything at all. But this type of scanner (under the Bearcat BC-50 title plus one or two others) has been quite popular among users such as marine band listeners who just want to keep an ear open on a few channels.

Realistic PRO-43
Type: Handheld
Coverage: 68–88, 118-174, 220–512, 806-1000 MHz
Modes: AM, FM
Channels: 200
Sensitivity: 145 MHz 0.26µV AM 0.13µV FM 435 MHz 0.83µV
                 AM 0.43µV FM 934 MHz 0.55µV AM 0.28µV FM
Adjacent channel: 12.5 kHz 7.0dB 25 kHz 33.3dB
Blocking: 100 kHz 44.5dB 1 MHz 71.2dB 10 MHz 94.0dB
Intermodulation: 50/100 kHz 49.7dB

Marketed as a high-performance scanner, this was the first handheld model from Realistic to have switchable AM and FM across its frequency coverage range. No longer do you have to put up with AM on airband only

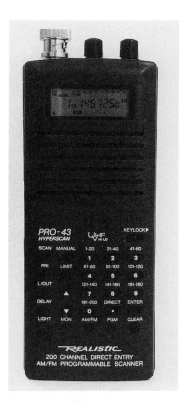

from high-street handheld scanners. A fast scanning facility together with 10 monitor memories in addition to the normal memory channels make it quite powerful in use. The set looks smart, it's easy to use, and as well as being very sensitive on VHF (to pick up weak signals), it also has reasonable built-in protection against out-of-band signals which many scanners fall down on badly.

Realistic PRO-62

Type:	Handheld
Coverage:	68–88, 118–174, 380–512, 806–960 MHz
Modes:	AM, FM
Channels:	200
Sensitivity:	145 MHz 0.22µV 435 MHz 0.37µV 935 MHz 0.46µV
Adjacent channel:	12.5 kHz 6.3dB 25 kHz 56.9dB
Blocking:	100 kHz 67.3dB 1 MHz 77.7dB 10 MHz 93.0dB
Intermodulation:	25/50 kHz 52.5dB 50/100 kHz 52.3dB

A reasonably lightweight handheld powered from 6 AA cells, with AM or FM programmable on any frequency as well as 5 kHz, 12.5 kHz or 25 kHz channel steps for search mode, although default mode and channel steps based on US use are initially selected when you change frequency.

Realistic PRO-63

Type:	Handheld
Coverage:	68–88, 118–174, 380–512 MHz
Modes:	AM airband, FM
Channels:	100
Sensitivity:	145 MHz 0.22µV 435 MHz 0.27µV
Adjacent channel:	12.5 kHz 8.4dB 25 kHz 64.7dB
Blocking:	100 kHz 74.9dB 1 MHz 85.1dB 10 MHz 87.6dB
Intermodulation:	25/50 kHz 58.2dB 50/100 kHz 57.8dB

This one is described as a portable event scanner due to its coverage range, as it could indeed be useful when you're out at the air show or yacht race. Fixed search banks act as an easy-to-use lookout for active channels, although again fixed 5 kHz steps are used on VHF.

Realistic PRO-70

Type:	Handheld
Coverage:	68–88, 137–174, 380–512 MHz
Modes:	AM, FM
Channels:	50
Sensitivity:	145 MHz 0.32µV 435 MHz 0.23µV
Adjacent channel:	12.5 kHz 8.7dB 25 kHz 56.8dB
Blocking:	100 kHz 58.1dB 1 MHz 95.0dB 10 MHz 93.5dB
Intermodulation:	25/50 kHz 52.5dB 50/100 kHz 52.3dB

Easy to use, FM-only scanner with 5 kHz steps on VHF and 12.5 kHz steps on UHF and nine pre-stored search banks, powered from six AA cells.

Realistic PRO-2006

Type:	Base/mobile
Coverage:	25–520, 760–1300 MHz
Modes:	AM, FM, Wide FM
Channels:	400
Sensitivity:	29 MHz 0.22μV FM 145 MHz 1.08μV FM 435 MHz 0.39μV FM 934 MHz 0.48μV FM
Adjacent channel:	12.5 kHz 27.5dB 25 kHz 50.3dB
Blocking:	100 kHz 69dB 1 MHz 88dB 10 MHz 94dB
Intermodulation:	50/100 kHz 66.5dB

From the number of these being snapped up by scanner purchasers when it first came out, this set looks like it's one of the most popular base scanners on the UK market. Switchable AM and FM across its coverage range gives it that bit more usefulness in the UK, and unlike earlier Realistic models you can choose step sizes of 5 kHz, 12.5 kHz, or 50 kHz. Although it's not one of the cheapest sets it works well on the air, and the wide frequency coverage is likely to make the set rival with other upmarket scanners available from specialist dealers.

Realistic PRO-2014

Type:	Base
Coverage:	68–88, 137–174, 380–512 MHz
Modes:	FM
Channels:	50
Sensitivity:	145 MHz 0.65μV FM 435 MHz 0.37μV FM
Adjacent channel:	12.5 kHz 7.4dB 25 kHz 62.8dB
Blocking:	100 kHz 66.3dB 1 MHz 91.7dB 10 MHz 94.2dB
Intermodulation:	25/50 kHz 56.5dB 50/100 kHz 56.8dB

Basically a base station model of one of Realistic's easy-to-use FM handhelds, not unlike the PRO-70 in facilities, with ten pre-stored search banks and 65 kHz steps on VHF, 12.5 kHz on UHF. A telescopic whip is supplied, the external aerial connector being a Motorola car-radio type.

Realistic PRO-2035

Type:	Base
Coverage:	25–520, 760–1300 MHz
Modes:	AM, FM, Wide FM
Channels:	1000
Sensitivity:	25 MHz 0.21µV FM 145 MHz 0.41µV FM 435 MHz 0.26µV FM 934 MHz 0.25µV FM
Adjacent channel:	12.5 kHz 0.7dB 25 kHz 24.2dB
Blocking:	100 kHz 55.4dB 1 MHz 78.2dB 10 MHz 88.6dB
Intermodulation:	25/50 kHz 58.7dB, 50/100 kHz 56.7dB

Together with keypad control, a rotary tuning knob also acts as a channel and frequency change for home use. A very fast scan rate of 50 channels per second, although the auto-store repeats previously found channels. Channel steps are selectable between 5, 12.5 and 25 kHz on any range, as well as selectable AM, FM and WFM modes.

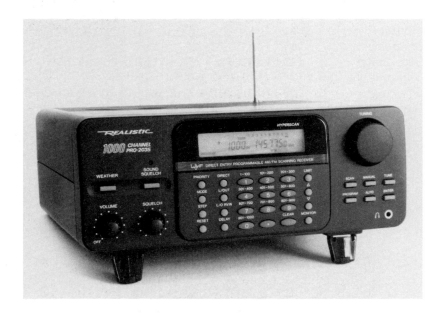

Realistic PRO-2036

Type: Base
Coverage: 66–88, 108–174, 216–512, 806–956 MHz
Modes: AM airband, FM
Channels: 200
Sensitivity: 145 MHz 0.34µV 435 MHz 0.26µV 950 MHz 0.23µV
                 FM
Adjacent channel: 12.5 kHz 7.6dB 25 kHz 60.8dB
Blocking: 100 kHz 75.5dB 1 MHz 84.0dB 10 MHz 86.7dB
Intermodulation: 25/50 kHz 55.9dB 50/100 kHz 63.4dB

A neatly styled base station scanner with the usual handheld facilities but with built-in CTCSS decode capability, which can also be used in scan mode to only halt and enable the speaker when the correct CTCSS tone is present on that channel. Realistic have overcome the PRO-2035's repeat store in auto-store memory mode with this one, as it works very well in the PRO-2036.

Realistic PRO-2045

Type: Base
Coverage: 68–88, 108–174, 216–512, 806–1000 MHz
Modes: AM, FM
Channels: 200
Sensitivity: 145 MHz 0.37µV 435 MHz 0.26µV 950 MHz 0.55µV
Adjacent channel: 12.5 kHz 7.7dB 25 kHz 51.0dB
Blocking: 100 kHz 51.9dB 1 MHz 82.6dB 10 MHz 96.6dB
Intermodulation: 25/50 kHz 61.5dB 50/100 kHz 62.3dB

This one has useful base station monitoring facilities such as a hit count mode to see how many times a channel has been active in your absence, a switchable attenuator, switchable AM and FM on any frequency, an auto-store that works well, and a search speed of an incredible 300 steps per second. Up to 50 channels can be programmed to be skipped on subsequent searches, but you're still limited to 5 kHz steps on VHF though unusually with 12.5 kHz rather than 25 kHz steps on VHF airband.

Realistic PRO-9200

Type:	Base
Coverage:	68–88, 108–174, 406–512 MHz
Modes:	AM airband, FM
Channels:	16
Sensitivity:	145 MHz 0.43µV 435 MHz 0.41µV
Adjacent channel:	12.5 kHz 8.5dB 25 kHz 63.5dB
Blocking:	100 kHz 76.5dB 1 MHz 90.0dB 10 MHz 96.5dB
Intermodulation:	25/50 kHz 67.0dB 50/100 kHz 65.5dB

An uncomplicated and easy-to-use scanner for the home, switching on immediately starts it off scanning thorough its 16 memory channels. There is also a search mode for finding new frequencies, with 5 kHz steps on VHF and 12.5 kHz steps on UHF, 25 kHz on airband. A car-radio type aerial connector is used for the supplied telescopic whip.

Shinwa SR-001

Type:	Base/mobile
Coverage:	25–1000 MHz
Modes:	AM, FM, Wide FM
Channels:	200
Sensitivity:	25 MHz 5.20µV AM 2.51µV FM 145 MHz 0.68µV AM 0.36µV FM 435 MHz 1.07µV AM 0.43µV FM 934 MHz 4.32µV AM 2.15µV FM
Adjacent channel:	12.5 kHz 26.0dB 25 kHz 53.0dB
Blocking:	100 kHz 76.5dB 1 MHz 88.5dB 10 MHz 96.5dB
Intermodulation:	25/50 kHz 50.5dB 50/100 kHz 68.8dB

This one looks like it was designed to be a hot contender for the alternative car radio market, although the manufacturer's choice of including a TV/video-style remote control with the radio is rather puzzling. Despite its features, this set doesn't quite seem to have caught on. Not a commonly found scanner but you might occasionally come across one secondhand.

Signal R535

Type:	Base/mobile/transportable
Coverage:	108–143, 220–380 MHz
Modes:	AM
Channels:	60

A specialised airband receiver with options available to enable it to be used while being carried around. A fairly tedious type of programming is involved but the set is highly spoken of by airband enthusiasts.

Sony Air-7

Type: Handheld
Coverage: 100 kHz 2.2 MHz, 76–
             136 MHz
Modes: AM, FM, Wide FM
Channels: 30

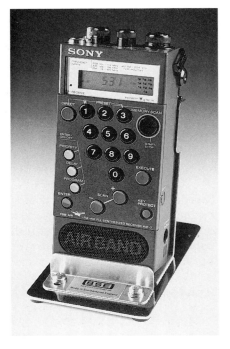

Bulky, heavy, limited coverage and expensive. However, airband fans say it performs superbly and the AGC (very important with AM) is excellent.

Sony PRO-80

Type: Handheld
Coverage: 150–108 MHz, 115–223MHz
Modes: AM, FM, SSB
Channels: 40

Similar in shape, size, and weight to the Air-7 and also expensive. Although the PRO-80 performs well, is built to Sony's usual high standard, and includes LW, MW plus full HF coverage, it does not include UHF. The VHF coverage is provided by a plug-in adapter, which seems to be an afterthought on the part of the designer.

Standard AX-400

Type: Portable
Coverage: 500–1300 MHz
Modes: AM, FM, Wide FM
Channels: 400
Sensitivity: 20 MHz 0.34µV AM 145 MHz 0.15µV FM 435 MHz
                   0.24µV FM 934 MHz 0.15µV FM
Adjacent channel: 12.5 kHz 24.8dB 25 kHz 54.1dB
Blocking: 100 kHz 54.0dB 1 MHz 83.2dB 10 MHz 94.0dB
Intermodulation: 25/50 kHz 52.6dB 50/100 kHz 55.8dB

A tiny wideband scanner, very easily portable, and powered by two AA-sized batteries. Standard seem to have a knack of squeezing circuitry into a small case without sacrificing on performance. The use of a standard BNC connector allows external mobile and portable aerials to be easily connected. I use one of these scanners myself as a top-pocket portable when I'm out and about. The Welz WS-1000 scanner is virtually identical.

Standard AX-700

Type: Base/mobile
Coverage: 50–905 MHz
Modes: AM, FM, Wide FM
Channels: 100
Sensitivity: 145MHz 0.39µV AM 0.18µV FM 435MHz 0.26µV
                   AM 0.25µV FM 905MHz 0.54µV AM 0.36µV FM
Adjacent channel: 12.5 kHz 31.0dB 25 kHz 65.3dB
Blocking: 100 kHz 73.0dB 1 MHz 78.0dB 10 MHz 100dB
Intermodulation: 50/100 kHz 58.5dB

If you fancy keeping an eye on what's going on above and below the channel you're tuned to, as well as listening to what you've tapped in on the keypad, this one's for you. It has a panoramic display in the form of a LCD bargraph, showing signal levels across a frequency range of 1 MHz, 250 kHz, or 100 kHz. Some users might find the 905 MHz upper frequency limiting.

Watson Super Searcher
A self-contained and portable frequency hunter which displays the frequency of signals it finds, in a similar manner to the Optoelectronics Scout, but without all the memories. With its data port it can also usefully connect with a suitably equipped scanner such as the AOR AR-8000 to automatically tune the set to the detected frequency.

Welz WS-1000

This is virtually identical to the Standard AX-400, detailed earlier.

WIN 108

Type:	Handheld
Coverage:	108–143MHz
Modes:	AM
Channels:	20

A scanner that has received mixed reactions. Some owners speak highly of it but some magazine reviews have been critical with claims that the keyboard is flimsy and difficult to operate, and sensitivity could be better on a set designed solely for AM mode.

Winradio

Type:	PC controlled
Coverage:	50 kHz–1300 MHz
Modes:	AM, FM, Wide FM, SSB
Sensitivity:	20 MHz 3.85µV SSB
	0.46µV AM 145 MHz
	0.86µV SSB 0.45µV
	AM 0.46µV FM 435
	MHz 0.29µV SSB 0.37µV AM 0.36µV FM 1300
	MHz 3.51µV SSB 2.39µV FM
Adjacent channel:	12.5 kHz 15.8dB 25 kHz 45.5dB
Blocking:	100 kHz 48.8dB 1 MHz 76.9dB 10 MHz 86.0dB
Intermodulation:	25/50 kHz 59.2dB 50/100 kHz 57.2dB

This comes as a plug-in PC card, fitting internally to your PC. On-screen tuning and memory facilities are controlled via the PC mouse and keyboard with unlimited memory channels and an auto-store facility. There's also a useful memory search where you can find memory channels by entering a partial text string. HF performance is naturally limited to that of a typical scanner rather than a purpose-designed HF receiver.

Yaesu FRG-9600

Type:	Base/mobile
Coverage:	60–950 MHz
Modes:	AM, FM, Wide FM, SSB
Channels:	100

One of the earliest non-Bearcat base station scanners from Japan, and many can be found secondhand being a very popular scanner in the early days. Some models have the advantage of a UK-fitted HF converter, useful with the included SSB mode, as well as extended UHF coverage above 905 MHz. The scan mode always continues 10 seconds after finding a signal which is limiting to some users, although a CAT computer control port on the rear panel extends the receiver's versatility.

Yupiteru VT-125
Type: Handheld
Coverage: 108–142 MHz
Modes: AM
Channels: 30

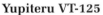

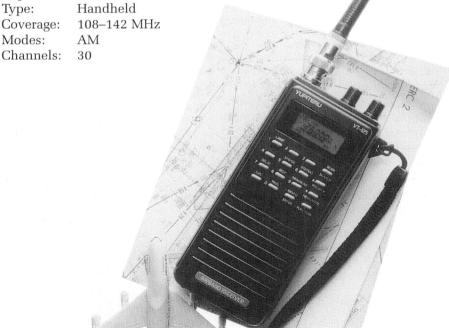

Sensitivity: 118 MHz 0.35μV 125 MHz 0.34μV 136 MHz 0.34μV
Adjacent channel: 25 kHz 60.8dB 50 kHz 66.3dB
Blocking: 100 kHz 70.0dB 1 MHz 89.0dB 10 MHz 84.5dB
Intermodulation: 25/50 kHz 50.5dB 50/100 kHz 50.0dB

This is a cut-down version, dedicated for civil airband listening, of Yupiteru's other do-everything handheld scanners. It's inexpensive and quite light and easy to carry around. Watch out for the narrow filtering, as this could distort some of the (deliberately) offset signals from land-based airband transmitters. The available 30 memory channels could be limiting for active airband enthusiasts.

Yupiteru VT-150
Type: Handheld
Coverage: 142–170 MHz
Modes: FM
Channels: 100

The dedicated marine band cousin to the airband VT-125 handheld scanner. Again it looks very much like a cut-down version of Yupiteru's do-everything handheld scanners, but without the higher price tag. A possible choice for the user interested primarily in marine band monitoring, although the 30 channels could be a bit limiting.

Yupiteru VT-225
Type: Handheld
Coverage: 108–142.1, 149.5–160,
                  222-391 MHz
Modes: AM, FM
Channels: 100
Sensitivity: 130 MHz 0.29μV AM
                  155 MHz 0.16μV FM
                  250 MHz 0.32μV
Adjacent channel: 12.5 kHz 48.3dB 25 kHz
                  52.0dB
Blocking: 100 kHz 63.5dB
                  1 MHz 91.0dB
                  10 MHz 94.5dB
Intermodulation: 25/50 kHz 53.0dB
                  50/100 kHz 62.5dB

This set from the Yupiteru collection looks like it is meant for airband (civil and military) and marine band enthusiasts – a bit of a mixture in fact. The manufacturer obviously feels that there is a niche market for such a set, and I believe they could well find it among users wanting a lightweight scanner to carry to air shows and the like.

Yupiteru MVT-3100

Type:	Handheld
Coverage:	143–162.025, 347.7125–452, 830–960 MHz
Modes:	FM
Channels:	100
Sensitivity:	145 MHz 0.21µV FM 435 MHz 0.18µV FM 934 MHz 0.35µV FM
Adjacent channel:	12.5 kHz 37.6dB 25 kHz 45.7dB
Blocking:	100 kHz 62.8dB 1 MHz 77.4dB 10 MHz 69.3dB
Intermodulation:	25/50 kHz 61.7dB 50/100 kHz 59.5dB

Another niche market set from Yupiteru, although quite what 'niche' I'm not too sure. It is hard programmed with 10 kHz steps over 143–155 MHz and 430–440 MHz, this includes the 2m and 70cm amateur bands, which instantly cuts out half of all the 25 kHz channels used. However, I found it to be a very good performer on 156 MHz marine band when I used it on the water, and the set very rapidly steps through programmed memory channels 30 at a time. A further useful feature is that it has up to 100 pass frequencies, which you can automatically program to skip with the set in search mode.

Yupiteru MVT-7000

Type:	Handheld
Coverage:	1–1300 MHz continuous
Modes:	AM, FM, Wide FM
Channels:	200
Sensitivity:	29 MHz 0.18µV FM 145 MHz 0.24µV FM 435 MHz 0.24µV FM 934 MHz 0.25µ V FM

Adjacent channel: 12.5 kHz 17.0dB 25 kHz 47.0dB
Blocking: 100 kHz 61.0dB 1 MHz 84.0dB 10 MHz 89.0dB
Intermodulation: 50/100 kHz 52.0dB

The tuning range of this set covers down to 100 kHz with reduced sensitivity, so as well as being a 'listen-to-everything on VHF/UHF' you can also tune into Medium Wave and HF broadcast stations for that bit of alternative listening. This one's a competitor in terms of frequency coverage to the IC-R1 and DJ-X1, and although it doesn't have the small size of its competition it doesn't have the poor performance of the others in terms of strong signal handling either. You pays your money and takes your choice.

Yupiteru MVT-7100
Type: Handheld
Coverage: 1–1300 MHz continuous
Modes: AM, FM, Wide FM, LSB, USB
Channels: 1000
Sensitivity: 20 MHz 0.16µV SSB 0.22µV AM 0.13µV FM
145 MHz 0.18µV SSB 0.25µV AM 0.16µV FM 435 MHz 0.26µV SSB 0.35µV AM 0.16µV FM
934 MHz 0.33µV SSB 0.37µV AM 0.21µV FM
Adjacent channel: 12.5 kHz 34.1dB 25 kHz 48.4dB
Blocking: 100 kHz 55.5dB 1 MHz 85.5dB 10 MHz 93.8dB
Intermodulation: 25/50 kHz 65.3dB 50/100 kHz 24.0dB

The very wide frequency coverage, together with real SSB reception and the ability to tune (and store frequencies) on SSB in 50 Hz steps, has made this a very sought-after set among scanner devotees. I've used one on many occasions, and I've always been sad to give it back, it just looks like I'll have to buy one of these when I've saved up. About the only thing I don't like about it is the telescopic whip, which will surely break in use, but at least this lets you adjust its

218

length to peak on the part of the set's very wide frequency range you're listening to at any given time.

Yupiteru MVT-7200

Type:	Handheld
Coverage:	500 kHz–1650 MHz continuous
Modes:	AM, FM, Wide FM, LSB, USB
Channels:	1000
Sensitivity:	20 MHz 0.16µV SSB 0.22µV AM 0.13µV FM 145 MHz 0.18µV SSB 0.25µV AM 0.16µV FM 435 MHz 0.26µV SSB 0.35µV AM 0.16µV FM 934 MHz 0.33µV SSB 0.37µV AM 0.21µV FM
Adjacent channel:	12.5 kHz 34.7dB 25 kHz 46.5dB
Blocking:	100 kHz 66.5dB 1 MHz 86.2dB 10 MHz 94.6dB
Intermodulation:	50/100 kHz 65.1dB

This is the physically similar successor to the MVT-7100 with almost similar facilities but an extended frequency coverage and significantly better IF filtering for SSB reception, also an added narrow AM bandwidth which is especially useful on the crowded HF bands. The easily breakable telescopic has also been sensibly replaced with a helical whip.

Yupiteru MVT-8000

Type:	Base/mobile
Coverage:	8–1300 MHz continuous
Modes:	AM, FM, Wide FM
Channels:	200

Essentially a base/mobile version of the Yupiteru MVT-7000, adding a switchable attenuator to help with strong signals from external aerials. It offers a wide frequency coverage in a very small case, which should fit quite neatly in your car as well as presenting a smart low profile on a desktop.

Yupiteru MVT-9000

Type:	Handheld
Coverage:	512 kHz–2039 MHz continuous
Modes:	AM, FM, Wide FM, LSB, USB, CW
Channels:	1000
Sensitivity:	20 MHz 0.09µV SSB 0.24µV AM 0.15µV FM 145 MHz 0.15µV SSB 0.36µV AM 0.23µV FM 435 MHz 0.22µV SSB 0.29µV FM 950 MHz 0.30µV SSB 0.44µV FM
Adjacent channel:	12.5 kHz 39.7dB 25 kHz 51.5dB
Blocking:	100 kHz 68.7dB 1 MHz 80.4dB 10 MHz 83.5dB
Intermodulation:	50/100 kHz 65.1dB

Yupiteru's top-of-the-range handheld, with both an external plug-in whip via a BNC connector and a selectable internal ferrite rod aerial for LF band portable reception. A dual frequency display, band-scope, and plenty of scanning and searching modes make this a very desirable and powerful handheld scanner. A built-in switchable speech inverter demodulates simple forms of scrambled transmissions.

AERIALS

Besides the usual aerials of dipoles, whips, discone and so on, detailed here are a few specialist aerials, which may be of interest to scanner users.

Product: Radac
Manufacturer: Revco (available from Garex)
This is what is known as a nest of dipoles type of antenna. It is quite an old idea which has been revamped to meet the needs of scanner users. In theory it provides reception on six bands which are determined by the length of each of the individual dipole sections. The manufacturers say that for those six bands, aerial gain will be better than a discone. Elements can be anywhere in the range 25–500 MHz.

Radac aerial

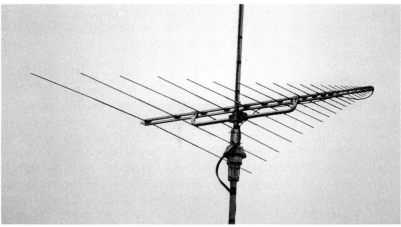

The Create CLP-5130-1 50–1300 MHz log-periodic, shown here mounted for horizontal polarisation

Product: Create CLP5130-2
Type: Log periodic
A 20 element log periodic aerial with coverage from 105 MHz to 1300 MHz. The gain is quoted as 11-13dB with a front to back ratio of 15dB. The aerial has a width of 1.4 metres and is 1.4 metres long. VSWR across the range is quoted as 2:1 and terminations are via an N-socket. Available from South Midlands Communications Ltd.

Product: Create CLP5130-1
Type: Log periodic
A wider band version of the above aerial covering 50–1300 MHz. A 24-element unit which is 3 metres wide and 2 metres long, otherwise the specifications are similar. Available from South Midlands Communications Ltd.

Product: Diamond D707
Type: Multiband pole
The aerial consists of a slim pole 95cm long which contains a broadband 20dB gain signal preamplifier. However, no details are given of the type of elements employed nor the performance across the range which is quoted as 2–1500 MHz. The aerial is supplied with a small power unit which sends voltage for the preamplifier up the coaxial feeder cable and some provision is made in the interface to vary the gain of the system. Available from Waters and Stanton.

Product: Diamond D505
Type: Multiband mobile aerial
Essentially a mobile version of the above aerial with the same specifications. The unit consists of a mobile mounting whip with two loading coils and built-in preamplifier. The aerial is 80cm long. Available from Waters and Stanton.

Sandpiper

Sandpiper manufacture an extremely wide range of aerials and it would be impossible to provide a complete list of their products. However, I would mention a few of their products which are of particular interest to scanner owners. First, they manufacture log periodics, discones and nests of dipoles (several versions of each covering different frequency ranges) as well as several versions of a multiband mobile aerial which can also be used as a base unit for anyone who cannot mount a discone. They can also supply high gain colinears for air and marine bands and the same bands are covered by a range of helical aerials for handsets. Because Sandpiper manufacture these products on a sort of modular basis they can supply helicals for instance, for any band with any type of plug (including right angle connections). Their range stretches to yagis and dipoles for virtually any frequency and again, because of the method of manufacture involved, costs are virtually the same as for an off-the-shelf product. Should you want to build your own antenna then Sandpiper can also supply both aluminium and fibreglass tubing as well as connector blocks and all the usual fittings. Again the range is so vast it is impossible to cover it here and you should contact them (address at the back of the book) and get a copy of their lists.

Replacement whips

About the most commonly damaged part of a portable scanner is, you've guessed it, the set-top whip. Garex and Nevada can supply a range of plug-in aerials for portable handhelds, including UHF and airband helicals. Garex can also supply helicals pre-tuned to the centre frequency of your choice.

Tunable aerial filter

Many of the scanners detailed in this book have an enormous frequency coverage in a very small package. But unfortunately selectivity and strong signal handling characteristics have sometimes been sacrificed to save space and cost, which means that unwanted signal breakthrough can be a big problem. Attaching a microscopic handheld to a rooftop aerial is often a good recipe for disappointment. One remedy from strong local signals but in a different band is to use a notch filter, which is a high-Q tuned circuit plugged-in line with the aerial and can be adjusted to attenuate an unwanted signal. One type, covering the 85–175 MHz range is marketed by Garex Electronics. It simply fits in line with the aerial feeder, and lets you tune unwanted signals out. Provided the interference is spaced more than 10 MHz away, there's little difference in the signal you want to hear.

Mobile scanner aerials

If you're using your handheld scanner on the move, then a suitable aerial fitted to the outside of the car can make a tremendous difference. Putting up with the set-top aerial is OK as a temporary measure, but you won't get the best from your scanner. Purpose-designed mobile scanners will, of course, always need some form of external aerial. Very often, a simple quarter wave whip, cut for the centre frequency of the band you're mainly interested in (such as civil airband), can make a reasonable all-round aerial for mobile scanner use. See Chapter 5 for details of lengths needed. Wideband aerials are a different matter though. A number of multiband aerials are available from amateur radio and scanner dealers, including wideband amplified types. A handy tip is that a dual band whip for the 2m and 70cm amateur bands makes a good all-round VHF/UHF mobile scanner aerial. If you'd prefer not to drill holes or clip aerial mounting brackets to your car gutter or boot lip, then a glass-mounted wideband aerial could be useful. A glassmount aerial sticks onto one of the windows of your car, usually the rear windscreen, using the glass as a dielectric between the inner and outer fittings. Waters and Stanton Electronics distribute what could be an ideal aerial, which is designed for wideband scanner receive-only use over 30–1200 MHz – the Pro-Am TGSBNC – which comes with everything you need right down to the BNC plug at the end of the length of coax. The aerial element itself can be unscrewed from its base for carwashes or security against other damage when not in use. If you're fitting one of these, make sure you get the position right first time (check the travel of windscreen wipers) as it's very difficult, if not impossible, to change once it's stuck! A re-mounting kit is, however, available should you change cars.

Pro-Am TGS BNC wideband scanner aerial

Aerial amplifiers

There are a number of wideband aerial preamps available, from firms such as Solid State Electronics and Garex. The latter, for example produce the GA-4M GAsFET amplifier covering 20–1000 MHz, and also produce a low-cost VHF airband preamplifier which is designed to cover 118–137 MHz with strong out-of-band signals attenuated. SSE supply the Jim series of preamplifiers which can be switched to either wideband or narrow, together plus other accessories such as handheld base and mobile mounts and chargers.

The Jim M-75 aerial amplifier

Indoor scanner aerials

If circumstances confine you to using indoor aerial, then try at least to get this near to a window – you'll usually notice a big improvement. A

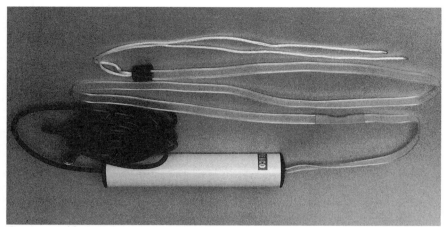

Garex portable aerial

popular portable VHF/UHF scanner aerial is the Nomad from Garex, which is available in normal and active amplified versions. It's a lightweight arrangement using ribbon cable elements and comes fitted with 4m of coax and a BNC plug – it is optimised for the VHF airband but works very well across the VHF/UHF range and is ideal for using your scanner from temporary locations as an improvement to a set-top whip. For VHF and HF reception, e.g. HF/VHF airband, then Solid State Electronics manufacture an excellent 'rollup and take it with you' wire aerial which uses a HF/VHF isolating section to give good performance on both ranges which comes complete with all the required hardware, insulators etc.

10 Scanner and accessory manufacturers, distributors and dealers

Listed below are a selection of UK and Eire based suppliers of scanners and accessories. Inclusion in this list does not suggest any recommendation or otherwise, also any omission of dealers doesn't mean they're not recommended or worthy of inclusion – it's just that I wasn't aware of their activity at the time of writing. For contact details of other suppliers local to you, just take a look in *Yellow Pages* under 'Radio Communications' and 'Aerials' or current adverts in specialist hobby radio publications, details of which are also given here.

Aerial Centre
188b Halfway Street
 Sidcup
Kent DA15 8DJ
Tel: 0181 300 5588.

Scanners and short wave receivers, aerials and accessories.

Aerial Techniques
11 Kent Road
Parkstone
Poole
Dorset BH12 2EH
Tel: 01202 738232
Email: atech@dircon.co.uk

Suppliers of masts, brackets, rotators and other aerial accessories.

AERI4L
9 Troopers Drive
Romford
Essex
Tel: 01708 374043

Specialists in secondhand equipment, listings available.

Air Supply
83B High Street
Yeadon
Leeds LS19 7TA
Tel: 01532 509581

Scanners, aero charts, aerials.

Amateur Radio Communications Limited

38 Bridge Street
Earlestown
Newton-le-Willows
Merseyside WA12 9BA
Tel: 01925 229881

Scanners, internal and external HF adaptors, antennae, books.

AOR (UK)

Adam Bede High Tech Centre
Derby Road
Wirksworth
Derbyshire DE4 4BG
Tel: 01629 825926
http://demon.co.uk/aor

UK distributors of AOR scanners, aerials, and PC control software for AOR scanners.

ARC Amateur Radio Communications

38 Bridge St
Earlestown
Newton-le-Willows
Merseyside WA12 9BA
Tel: 01925 229881
http://arcoms.force9.co.uk

Scanners, aerials, secondhand equipment also stocked.

ASK Electronics

248/250 Tottenham Court Road
London W1P 9AD
Tel: 0171 637 0353

HF receivers, scanners, accessories and books.

Aviation Hobby Centre

Visitor Centre
Main Terminal, Birmingham
International Airport
W Midlands B26 3QJ
Tel: 0121 742 0424
http://www.users.zetnet.co.uk/
hobbyctr

Scanners, aerials and books.

Cirkit Distribution

Park Lane
Broxbourne
Herts EN10 7NQ
Tel: 01992 444111

Scanners, books, RF plugs, sockets and components.

Flightdeck

192 Wilmslow Road
Heald Green
Cheadle
Cheshire SK8 3BH
Tel: 0161 499 9350
Email: FlightDek@aol.com

Scanners, aero charts and books, aerials.

Flying Shop

Biggin Hill Airport
Westerham
Kent TN16 3BN
Tel: 01959 576370

Airband guides and scanners.

Garex Electronics

Unit 8 Sandpiper Court
Harrington Lane
Exeter EX4 8NS
Tel: 01392 466899

Scanners, manufacturers and suppliers of scanner aerial systems, preamps and filters.

Haydon Communications
132 High Street
Edgware
Middlesex HA8 7EL
Tel: 0181 951 5782

*Scanners and accessories, HF
specialist, retail branch also in
West Midlands.*

ICOM (UK)
Sea Street
Herne Bay
Kent CT6 8LD
Tel: 01227 741741
http://icomuk.co.uk

*UK Distributors of Icom scanners,
receivers and aerials.*

ICS Electronics
Unit V Rudford Industrial Estate
 Ford
Arundel
West Sussex BN18 0BD
Tel: 01903 731101

*Fax and multi-mode data
decoders.*

Interproducts
8 Abbot Street
Perth PH2 0EB
Scotland
Tel: 01738 44199
Email:
mailto:interproducts@netmatters.
co.uk

*Wide range of books and frequency
lists, publishers of the very comprehensive UK Scanning Directory.*

Javiation
Carlton Works
Carlton Street
Bradford
West Yorkshire BD7 1DA
Tel: 01274 732146
http://javation.co.uk

*Scanners, aerials, aviation charts,
frequency lists, preamps, airband
crystals.*

Lar Communications Centre
Bradford Road
East Ardsley
Wakefield WF3 2DN
Tel: 0113 252 4586

*Scanners, short-wave receivers,
aerials and accessories.*

Link Electronics
216 Lincoln Road
Peterborough PE1 2NE
Tel: 01733 345731

*Scanners, aerials, and specialist
suppliers of Netset and Realistic
products.*

Links Communications
Crossways Centre
Braye Road
Vale
Guernsey CI
Tel: 01481 48360

*Scanners and aerials (VAT-free
export).*

Lowe Electronics
Chesterfield Road
Matlock
Derbyshire DE4 5LE
Tel: 01629 580800
http://www.lowe.co.uk

*Scanners, HF receivers, HF
and VHF/UHF aerials, JRC
distributors, branches in Bristol
and Newcastle.*

Maplin Electronics
PO Box 777
Rayleigh
Essex SS6 8LU
Tel: 01702 554000
http://www.maplin.co.uk

*Scanners and receivers, wide
range of plugs, connectors, power
supplies, nicads, books, aerial
fittings etc. Retail shops throughout
the UK.*

Martin Lynch and Sons
140–142 Northfield Avenue
Ealing
London W13 9SB
Tel: 0181 566 1120
http://www.MLandS.co.uk

*Scanners, aerials, books, large
range of secondhand equipment.*

Moonraker UK
Unit 12
Cranfield Road Units
Cranfield Road
Woburn Sands
Bucks MK17 8UR
Tel: 01908 281705

Suppliers of wideband aerials.

Multicom 2000
Unit 5–7
86 Cambridge Street
St. Neots
Cambs PE19 1PJ
Tel: 01480 406770
http://www.multicomm2000.com

*Scanners and books, aerials,
worldwide mail order facilities.*

Nevada Communications
189 London Road
North End
Portsmouth PO2 9AE
Tel: 01705 662145
http://www.nevada.co.uk

*Scanners (agents for Alinco,
Optoelectronics, Uniden, Yupiteru),
books, aerials, pre-amps, large
range of secondhand equipment.*

Photavia Press
Sunrise Break
Chisledon Farm
Southdown Hill
Brixham
Devon TQ5 0AE
Tel: 01803 855599

*Publishers of up-to-date airband
frequency directories and civil/
military callsign directories.*

QSL Communications
Unit 6 Worle Industrial Centre
Coker Road
Worle
Weston-Super-Mare BS22 6BX
Tel: 01934 512757

*Scanners and short-wave receiv-
ers, aerials and accessories.*

QSP 73 Services
PO Box 400
Eastleigh
Hants SO53 4ZF
Tel: 01703 263429
http://www.qsp73.demon.co.uk

Suppliers of CD-ROM collections of the latest freeware, shareware, and public domain hobby radio PC software.

Radcom Electronics
Middleton Enterprise Park
Middleton
Co. Cork
Tel: (Eire) 021 632725

Scanners, aerials, preamps.

Radio Amateur Supplies (Nottingham)
3 Farndon Green
Woollaton Park
Nottingham NH8 1DU
Tel: 0115 928 0267
http://www.geocities.com/Eureka/1448

Scanners, aerials.

Radioworld
37 Coppice Lane
Cheslyn Hay
Walsall
West Midlands WS6 7HA
Tel: 01922 414796
http://www.freespace.virgin.net/radio.world

Scanners and accessories, large range of secondhand equipment.

Reg Ward & Co
1 Westminster House
West Street
Axminster
Devon EX13 5NX
Tel: 01297 34918
http://www.smc-comms.com/amateur

Scanners, aerials, large range of secondhand equipment.

Sandpiper Communications
Pentwyn House
Penyard Llwydcoed
Aberdare
Mid Glamorgan CF44 0TU
Tel: 01685 870425

Aerial manufacturers.

Seaward Electronics
Kings Hill Industrial Estate
Bude
Cornwall
Tel: 01288 55998

Scanners, aerials and accessories.

Shortwave Shop
18 Fairmile Road
Christchurch
Dorset BH23 2IJ
Tel: 01202 490099
http://www.shortwave.co.uk

Receivers, scanners, airband and marine receivers.

Solid State Electronics
6 The Orchard
Bassett Green Village
Southampton SO2 3NA
Tel: 01703 769598

Manufacturers of preamps, and accessories for handheld scanners such as chargers, desk stands and mobile mounts.

South East Communications
The Anchorage
Williamstown Road
Waterford
Rep of Ireland
Tel: (Eire) 051 871278.

*Scanners and accessories, large
range of secondhand equipment.*

South Midlands Communications
SM House
School Close
Chandlers Ford Industrial Estate
Eastleigh
Hampshire SO5 3BY
Tel: 01703 246222
http://www.smc-comms.com

*Scanners, aerials, converters and
frequency guides, HF specialists,
manufacturers of HF receivers,
large range of secondhand
equipment.*

SRP Trading
1686 Bristol Road South
Rednal
Birmingham B45 9TZ
Tel: 0121 460 1581

*Suppliers of scanners, books, and
their unique types of discone
aerials.*

Stephens James
47 Warrington Road
Leigh
Lancashire WN7 3AE
Tel: 01942 676790

Scanners, aerials and fitting kits.

Tandy/Antika Retail Limited
Tandy Centre
Leamore Lane
West Midlands WS2 7PS

*Suppliers of Realistic scanners.
Tandy shops are located throughout
Britain, check your area telephone
directory for the nearest branch.*

Timestep Communications
PO Box 2001
Newmarket
Cambs CB8 8XB
Email: mailto: sales@time-step.com

*Receivers, aerials, and PC-based
systems for weather satellite reception.*

Unicom
112 Reculver Road
Beltinge
Herne Bay
Kent CT6 6PD
Tel: 01227 749038
http://www.cqdx.co.uk/unicom

*Scanners, antennas, Icom special-
ists, agents also for AOR, Alinco,
Kenwood and Yaesu.*

Waters & Stanton
22 Main Road
Hockley
Essex SS5 4QS
Tel: 01702 206835/204965
http://www.waters-and-
stanton.co.uk

*Scanners, preamps, converters,
books (list publishers), aerials
including glass-mount mobile type,
agents for Optoelectronics and
Yupiteru, large range of secondhand
equipment.*

NATIONAL ORGANISATIONS

AMSAT-UK
40 Downsview
Small Dole
West Sussex BN5 9YB
http://www.uk.amsat.org

Amateur Satellite Organisation – a voluntary non-profit-making organisation dedicated to the furtherance of amateur radio satellites. They publish an excellent bi-monthly newsletter. Membership information available by sending an SAE to the above address.

ISWL (International Short Wave League)
1 Jersey Street
Hafpod
Swansea SA1 2HF
Tel: 01792 426449
http://home.aol.com/ILAweb

A group dedicated to the interests of radio listening worldwide, they publish a quarterly newsletter and run a number or scanner and short-wave listening contests each year.

Radio Society of Great Britain
Lambda House
Cranbourne Road
Potters Bar
Herts EN6 3JE
Tel. 01707 659015
http://www.rsgb.co.uk

The UK's national group representing radio amateurs and their interests, also publishers of Radio Today *magazine and a number of radio-related books.*

Radiocommunications Agency
South Quay Three
189 Marsh Wall
London E14 9SX
Tel: 0171 211 2110
http://www.open.gov.uk/radiocom/rahome.htm

The UK's radio regulatory body – they can supply the Receive-Only Scanners Etc. information sheet.

Remote Imaging Group
34 Ellington Road
Surbiton
Surrey KT6 7TX
http://www.rig.org.uk

International group for weather satellite and fax reception) who publish a quarterly newsletter and cater for the interests of weather satellite enthusiasts.

MONTHLY MAGAZINES

Radio Today
RSGB Publications
Lambda House
Cranbourne Road
Potters Bar
Herts EN6 3JE
Tel: 01707 853300
http://www.rsgb.org/hrt

Amateur radio and listener maga-zine.

Radio Active
Radio Active Publications
189 London Road
North End
Portsmouth
Hants PO2 9AE
Tel: 01705 613800
http://www.radio-active.co.uk

Lively all-round hobby radio magazine.

Practical Wireless
PW Publishing
Arrowsmith Court
Station Approach
Broadstone
Dorset BH18 8PW
Tel. 01202 659910
http://www.pwpublishing.ltd.uk

Amateur radio-based sister maga-zine to Short Wave Magazine.

Short Wave Magazine
PW Publishing
Arrowsmith Court
Station Approach
Broadstone
Dorset BH18 8PW
Tel. 01202 659910
http://www.pwpublishing.ltd.uk

Specialist listener magazine.

▉11▉ Scanners 2

Scanners 2 is the perfect match to the book you are reading now. It is an international edition that goes into the subject of the more advanced scanner user and also covers VHF/UHF monitor receivers. Here are some of the subjects that are covered:

Modifications

Simultaneous AM/FM for the SX-200 and Bearcat 220FB.

Common faults

SX-200 (various improvements), Bearcat 220 (power supply), AOR 2001 (off frequency), etc.

DIY accessories

Active antenna, SX-200 front panel S-Meter, BFO, broadband and narrow band masthead amplifiers, power supplies, auto-nicad charger, 12V to 6V or 9V adaptor for portables and automatic recording switch.

Project

Build a 10-channel crystal-controlled pocket or mobile scanner. Easy-to-build VHF/FM design that uses parts available from regular component suppliers.

Computer control

A detailed look at the advantages of using a personal computer to control a scanner (AOR 2002, ICOM, SX-400, etc.).

DXing

Using your scanner for long-distance reception. How to recognise the signs that a lift is on, where to tune and hear stations from as far away as the USA under the right conditions. List of VHF broadcast stations, beacons, repeaters, etc.

Spectrum

Full international spectrum allocations for all three ITU regions from 26–1300 MHz.

Callsigns

Full list of international, air and marine callsigns and registrations.

Airports

Spot frequencies of the world's major airports.

12 HF bandplans

As many scanners now cover the HF (Short Wave) spectrum as well as VHF/UHF, below is a HF bandplan to provide a guide to international allocations in each region. Region 1 covers the UK and Europe, although use in Regions 2 and 3 (the rest of the world) are also given due to the international radio propagation which occurs on HF.

Table 12.1

Region 1 From To	Region 2 From To	Region 3 From To
	1605 1625	
1606.5 1625	Broadcasting	**1606.5 1800**
Maritime mobile	Fixed	Mobile
Fixed		Radiolocation
Land mobile		Radionavigation
1625 1635	**1625 1705**	
Radiolocation	Broadcasting	
	Fixed	
	Mobile	
1635 1800		
Maritime mobile	**1705 1800**	
Fixed	Fixed	
Land mobile	Mobile	
	Radiolocation	
	Aeronavigation	
1800 1810	**1800 1850**	**1800 2000**
Radiolocation	Amateur	Amateur
	Radionavigation	Fixed
1810 1850	Radiolocation	Mobile (not aero)
Amateur		

237

Region 1		Region 2		Region 3	
From	To	From	To	From	To
1850	**2000**	**1850**	**2000**		
Fixed		Amateur			
Mobile (not aero)		Fixed			
		Mobile (not aero)			
		Radiolocation			
		Radionavigation			
2000	**2025**	**2000**	**2065**	**2000**	**2065**
Fixed		Fixed		Fixed	
Mobile (not aero)		Mobile		Mobile	
2025	**2045**				
Fixed					
Mobile (not aero)					
Meteorological aids					
2045	**2160**				
Maritime mobile		**2065**	**2107**	**2065**	**2107**
Fixed		Maritime mobile		Maritime mobile	
Land mobile					
		2107	**2170**	**2107**	**2170**
2160	**2170**	Fixed		Fixed	
Radiolocation		Mobile		Mobile	
2170	**2173.5**	**2170**	**2173.5**	**2170**	**2173.5**
Maritime mobile		Maritime mobile		Maritime mobile	
2173.5	**2190.5**	**2173.5**	**2190.5**	**2173.5**	**2190.5**
Mobile (distress)		Mobile (distress)		Mobile (distress)	
2190.5	**2194**	**2190.5**	**2194**	**2190.5**	**2194**
Maritime mobile		Maritime mobile		Maritime mobile	
2194	**2300**	**2194**	**2300**	**2194**	**2300**
Fixed		Fixed		Fixed	
Mobile (not aero)		Mobile		Mobile	
2300	**2498**	**2300**	**2495**	**2300**	**2495**
Fixed		Fixed			
Mobile (not aero)		Mobile			
Broadcasting		Broadcasting			
2498	**2502**	**2495**	**2502**	**2495**	**2502**
Standard frequency & time sig (2500 kHz)		Standard frequency & time sig (2500 kHz)		Standard frequency & time sig (2500 kHz)	
Space research		Space research		Space research	
2502	**2625**	**2502**	**2505**	**2502**	**2505**
Fixed		Standard frequency & time sig (2500 kHz)		Standard frequency & time sig (2500 kHz)	
Mobile (not aero)					

Region 1		Region 2		Region 3	
From	To	From	To	From	To
		2505	**2850**	**2505**	**2850**
		Fixed		Fixed	
2625	**2650**	Mobile		Mobile	
Maritime mobile					
Maritime					
Radionavigation					
2650	**2850**				
Fixed					
Mobile (not aero)					
2850	**3155**	**2850**	**3155**	**2850**	**3155**
Aeronautical mobile		Aeronautical mobile		Aeronautical mobile	
3155	**3200**	**3155**	**3200**	**3155**	**3200**
Fixed		Fixed		Fixed	
Mobile (not aero)		Mobile (not aero)		Mobile (not aero)	
3200	**3230**	**3200**	**3230**	**3200**	**3230**
Fixed		Fixed		Fixed	
Mobile (not aero)		Mobile (not aero)		Mobile (not aero)	
Broadcasting		Broadcasting		Broadcasting	
3230	**3400**	**3230**	**3400**	**3230**	**3400**
Fixed		Fixed		Fixed	
Mobile (not aero)		Mobile (not aero)		Mobile (not aero)	
Broadcasting		Broadcasting		Broadcasting	
3400	**3500**	**3400**	**3500**	**3400**	**3500**
Aeronautical mobile		Aeronautical mobile		Aeronautical mobile	
3500	**3800**	**3500**	**3750**	**3500**	**4000**
Amateur		Amateur		Amateur	
Fixed		Mobile		Fixed	
Mobile (not aero)					
		3750	**4000**		
		Amateur			
3800	**3900**	Fixed			
Fixed		Mobile (not aero)			
Mobile (not aero)					
Land mobile					
3900	**3950**	**3900**	**3950**		
Aeronautical mobile		Aeronautical mobile			
		Broadcasting			
3950	**4000**	**3950**	**4000**		
Fixed		Fixed			
Broadcasting		Broadcasting			
4000	**4063**	**4000**	**4063**	**4000**	**4063**
Fixed		Fixed		Fixed	
Maritime mobile		Maritime mobile		Maritime mobile	

Region 1		Region 2		Region 3	
From	To	From	To	From	To
4063	**4438**	**4063**	**4438**	**4063**	**4438**
Maritime mobile		Maritime mobile		Maritime mobile	
4438	4650	4438	4650	4438	4650
Fixed		Fixed		Fixed	
Mobile (not aero)		Mobile (not aero)		Mobile (not aero)	
4650	**4750**	**4650**	**4750**	**4650**	**4750**
Aeronautical mobile		Aeronautical mobile		Aeronautical mobile	
4750	**4850**	**4750**	**4850**	**4750**	**4850**
Fixed		Fixed		Fixed	
Aeronautical mobile		Mobile (not aero)		Broadcasting	
Land mobile		Broadcasting		Land mobile	
Broadcasting					
4850	**4995**	**4850**	**4995**	**4850**	**4995**
Fixed		Fixed		Fixed	
Land mobile		Land mobile		Land mobile	
Broadcasting		Broadcasting		Broadcasting	
4995	**5005**	**4995**	**5005**	**4995**	**5005**
Standard frequency & time sig (5000 kHz)		Standard frequency & time sig (5000 kHz)		Standard frequency & time sig (5000 kHz)	
5005	**5060**	**5005**	**5060**	**5005**	**5060**
Fixed		Fixed		Fixed	
Broadcasting		Broadcasting		Broadcasting	
5060	**5250**	**5060**	**5250**	**5060**	**5250**
Fixed		Fixed		Fixed	
Mobile (not aero)		Mobile (not aero)		Mobile (not aero)	
5250	**5450**	**5250**	**5450**	**5250**	**5450**
Fixed		Fixed		Fixed	
Mobile (not aero)		Mobile (not aero)		Mobile (not aero)	
5450	**5480**	**5450**	**5480**	**5450**	**5480**
Fixed		Aeronautical mobile		Fixed	
Aeronautical mobile				Aeronautical mobile	
Land mobile				Land mobile	
5480	**5730**	**5480**	**5730**	**5480**	**5730**
Aeronautical mobile		Aeronautical mobile		Aeronautical mobile	
5730	**5950**	**5730**	**5950**	**5730**	**5950**
Fixed		Fixed		Fixed	
Land mobile		Mobile (not aero)		Mobile (not aero)	
5950	**6200**	**5950**	**6200**	**5950**	**6200**
Broadcasting		Broadcasting		Broadcasting	
6200	**6525**	**6200**	**6525**	**6200**	**6525**
Maritime mobile		Maritime mobile		Maritime mobile	

Region 1		Region 2		Region 3	
From	To	From	To	From	To
6525	**6765**	**6525**	**6765**	**6525**	**6765**
Aeronautical mobile		Aeronautical mobile		Aeronautical mobile	
6765	**7000**	**6765**	**7000**	**6765**	**7000**
Fixed		Fixed		Fixed	
Land mobile		Land mobile		Land mobile	
7000	**7100**	**7000**	**7100**	**7000**	**7100**
Amateur		Amateur		Amateur	
Amateur-satellite		Amateur-satellite		Amateur-satellite	
7100	**7300**	**7100**	**7300**	**7100**	**7300**
Broadcasting		Amateur		Broadcasting	

Above 7300 kHz allocations for all three regions are identical.

From	To	Allocation
7300	**8100**	Fixed and land mobile
8100	**8195**	Fixed and maritime mobile
8195	**8815**	Maritime mobile
8815	**9040**	Aeronautical mobile
9040	**9500**	Fixed
9500	**9900**	Broadcasting
9900	**9995**	Fixed
9995	**10005**	Standard frequency & time sig (10000 kHz)
10005	**10100**	Aeronautical mobile
10100	**10150**	Fixed and amateur
10150	**11175**	Fixed and mobile (not aero)
11175	**11400**	Aeronautical mobile
11400	**11650**	Fixed
11650	**12050**	Broadcasting
12050	**12230**	Fixed
12230	**13200**	Maritime mobile
13200	**13360**	Aeronautical mobile
13360	**13410**	Fixed and radio astronomy
13410	**13600**	Fixed and mobile (not aero)
13600	**13800**	Broadcasting
13800	**14000**	Fixed mobile (not aero)
14000	**14250**	Amateur, amateur-satellite
14250	**14350**	Amateur
14350	**14990**	Fixed, mobile (not aero)
14990	**15010**	Standard frequency & time sig (15000 kHz)
15010	**15100**	Aeronautical mobile
15100	**15600**	Broadcasting
15600	**16360**	Fixed
16360	**17410**	Maritime mobile
17410	**17550**	Fixed
17550	**17900**	Broadcasting
17900	**18030**	Aeronautical mobile

From	To	Allocation
18030	**18068**	Fixed and space research
18068	**18168**	Amateur and amateur-satellite
18168	**18780**	Fixed
18780	**18900**	Maritime mobile
18900	**19680**	Fixed
19680	**19800**	Maritime mobile
19800	**19990**	Fixed
19990	**20010**	Standard frequency & time sig (20000 kHz), space research
20010	**21000**	Fixed and mobile
21000	**21450**	Amateur and amateur-satellite
21450	**21850**	Broadcasting
21850	**21870**	Fixed
21870	**21924**	Aeronautical fixed
21924	**22000**	Aeronautical mobile
22000	**22855**	Maritime mobile
22855	**23000**	Fixed
23000	**23200**	Fixed and mobile (not aero)
23200	**23350**	Aeronautical fixed and mobile
23350	**24000**	Fixed and mobile (not aero)
24000	**24890**	Fixed and land mobile
24890	**24990**	Amateur and amateur-satellite
24990	**25010**	Standard frequency & time sig (25000 kHz), space research
25010	**25070**	Fixed and mobile (not aero)
25070	**25210**	Maritime mobile
25210	**25550**	Fixed and mobile (not aero)
25550	**25670**	Radio astronomy
25670	**26100**	Broadcasting
26100	**26175**	Maritime mobile
26175	**27500**	Fixed and mobile (not aero)
27500	**28000**	Meteorological aids, fixed and mobile (CB)
28000	**29700**	Amateur and amateur-satellite
29700	**30005**	Fixed and mobile
30005	**30010**	Space operation (satellite identification) fixed, mobile and space research
30010	**37500**	Fixed and mobile

▮ Index